X 11

B 4

help from British, Dutch and American scientists.

Corrects Charts

The Albatross' pride and joy was an automatic graph which drew in ink a profile of the ocean floor, the result correcting many misconceptions of the underwater mountains previously charted. Also, for the first time, the Albatross tested back samples of sediment in up to 65-foot hunks, instead of the mere handfuls, all that could be gathered from earlier instruments. This contribution alone gave scientists extensive knowledge for geology, mineralogy, biology and radioactivity.

The ship traveled more than 45,000 nautical miles and most of the 15 months was spent probing in the Atlantic, Pacific and Indian oceans. Doctor Pettersson holds the chair of oceanography at the University of G Sweden, and has lectured versities around the wor was in the United States to deliver the Silliman le Yale University.

Houston Chronicle
January 10, 1954

WESTWARD HO WITH THE *ALBATROSS*

Frontispiece

THE *ALBATROSS* UNDER CANVAS

WESTWARD HO
WITH THE
ALBATROSS

BY

HANS PETTERSSON

Leader of
the Swedish Deep-Sea Expedition

ILLUSTRATED

NEW YORK
E. P. DUTTON & CO., INC.
1953

CONTENTS

5

ILLUSTRATIONS

(PLATES)

6

CHARTS AND SKETCHES

PREFACE

For generations my people have been working by the sea, on the sea, and struggling with its problems. Our ancestral home, "Kålhuvudet," which is Swedish for "head of cabbage"—a name which well describes the shape of the rocky islet on which it's built—is a very old wooden house far out on the storm-swept coast of the Skagerak. It has miraculously escaped being burnt down, a fate which sooner or later befalls the wooden huts and houses of my native province of Bohuslan.

The house lies so close to deep water that during the Napoleonic wars, in the days of my great-grandfather, a ship was wrecked immediately in front of it. The captain, with his wife and their infant son, and the crew as well, got ashore along the bowsprit, which had rammed the kitchen window. The site is a lovely one, open to the wide sea. Through the small panes of the modest windows—glass was scarce at the time when the house was built—sweeps by night the powerful beam from the "Pater Noster" Lighthouse, illuminating the age-old rooms. The name of this lighthouse is significant. The crew of a ship drifting with the strong current against its wicked rocks had excellent reasons for saying their prayers. In fact "Kålhuvudet" to a large extent is furnished with quaint old furniture salvaged from wrecks in bygone ages when the Lord had blessed the poor fisher-folk by allowing a good ship to come to grief on their rocky shores.

That the house is full of ghosts goes without saying. Not being gifted with second sight, I have never seen any. And yet, lying awake on a stormy night, when a gale from the west makes the ancient timber in the walls creak and groan in every joint, I feel quite ready to believe the gruesome stories told by the fireside when I was a boy.

With such ancestry and in such an environment, the sea is bound to become an obsession, as it was with my father, a renowned oceanographer who was eager to probe its mysteries to the time of his death at the ripe age of nearly ninety-three. He had devoted the greater part of his life's work to the sea around Scandinavia and northwestern Europe, and had brought into being the International Council for the Investigation of the Sea. My own preference was ever for the great ocean depths, about which we know practically nothing. Meeting that grand old man of deep-sea research, Sir John Murray of *Challenger* fame, during my student year with Sir William Ramsay in London, had kindled my imagination and my longing to grapple with the mysteries of the ocean floor.

But alas, the study of the deep sea calls for stupendous resources, including a large ocean-going ship fully equipped for research. The prospect of ever seeing my dreams of a Swedish deep-sea expedition realized appeared very remote. Well into the 1930's my work had to be along the lines my father had followed, investigating the water layers round our coasts, their currents and the curious submarine waves he had discovered in the Gullmar Fiord from the research station on Bornö.

But cherished dreams of one's boyhood sometimes do come true. Through articles in the press, by broadcasts and by popular science books, the fight for the Science of the Sea was carried on for years. A well-known Swedish banker and statesman, K. A. Wallenberg, and his wife, gave large sums to the Royal Society of Göteborg which made it possible to build and equip an excellent laboratory, *Oceanografiska Institutet*. There the weapons for a coming attack on the problems of the deep sea were forged. There also I found excellent co-workers who gave valuable help in the planning of our coming cruise.

World War II cut us off from work in the open sea but, by way of compensation, gave us time and opportunities for preparing a round-the-world cruise. The wealthy men of Göteborg have always been generous to the arts and sciences. One of them, Major Herbert Jacobsson, chairman of the great Broström shipping combine, and his wife, *née* Broström, bequeathed to the Royal Society of Göteborg half a million Swedish kronor (about $98,000 at the normal rate of exchange) toward the cost of a Swedish deep-sea expedition. A textile and commerce magnate, Mr. Gustaf Werner, gave a sum twice as large for the same purpose. Major Jacobsson also induced the Broström combine to lend us their excellent new training-ship, the motor-schooner *Albatross*, at net running cost for a cruise estimated to require fifteen months. In addition, we were allowed to have her fitted out as a floating laboratory of high efficiency at the Lindholmen Shipyard where she had been built. This very costly conversion of the space otherwise used for cargo into cabins, mess-room, laboratories, etc., as well as the mounting of our unique deep-sea winch and the electric plant required for working it, was made

possible through the generosity of Mr. Axelsson Johns-
son of Stockholm.

Our whole enterprise thus was financed by private
donors without any support from the Swedish Government. To the generosity of these men of wealth and
vision and to the generous collaboration of various leading Swedish firms who gave us the highest priority for
making our equipment we owe the material basis of our
enterprise, the first deep-sea expedition under the Swedish flag.

HANS PETTERSSON

Kålhuvudet

WESTWARD HO WITH THE *ALBATROSS*

Chapter 1

THE BEGINNING OF THINGS

Some three thousand million years ago our Earth was torn out of the body of her mother the Sun by a stupendous cosmic catastrophe, due to an encounter with a vagrant star, an unknown father of a whole family of planets. In this family our Earth occupies an intermediate position, both with regard to her size and to her distance from the Sun. A glowing globe of incandescent gas, she rapidly cooled, like a live coal raked out of a fire. Within a few thousand years—the mere twinkling of an eye on the cosmic time-scale—the cooling effect of radiation into space transformed her into a dark body with a remnant of solar heat buried beneath a solid crust. Gradually the surface temperature fell still lower until enormous masses of hot water were condensed from the primeval atmosphere, and so the ocean was born.

Since that remote past our Earth has remained the water planet, just as her nearest neighbors among the heavenly hosts, the dazzling white star of love, Venus, may be called the cloud planet, and Mars, the fiery red star of war, the desert planet. Venus, shrouded in impenetrable clouds, is probably still in her pre-oceanic stage, whereas Mars is supposed to have lost his original supply of water, which is now largely combined with the chemical compounds in the crust.

It is possible that in a very distant future a similar desiccation will overcome our Earth, leaving her bare and devoid of oceans [1]—a dismal prospect indeed, especially for us oceanographers, who by that time will have had to find some other occupation. In her present, fortunately moist, state, the Earth exposes to the surrounding Universe a surface of which more than 70 per cent is covered with water—no doubt an object of wonder and envy to inhabitants, if such there be, of other worlds who may happen to possess powerful telescopes.

It would be rash to assume that the terrestrial globe representing our Earth today gives a true picture of her features when she was still in her youth. The surface has undergone enormous changes. The crust has contracted and cracked, as the inexorable radiation losses reduced the temperature of her interior, slowly dissipating her inheritance of solar heat. Moreover, the ocean surface has risen and fallen, sometimes inundating the lowlands around its shores, at other times retreating and laying bare the bottom of the shallow coastal seas covered with sediments carried out into the sea by the rivers and consisting of the finest fragments from the remains of mountains. After periods of millions of years, enormous forces arising in the shrinking crust have lifted these

[1] Since in the realms of natural science there are almost always two opposite views of the same problem, it is only fair to admit that many, perhaps the majority, of leading geologists today regard the pessimistic view of our Earth going dry as incorrect. They assume instead the amount of water in the oceans to be steadily growing, because of a surplus of magmatic water disengaged from volcanoes. To this reassuring view reference will be made in a later chapter.

marine deposits high into the air and crumpled them to
form lofty mountain chains, as a tablecloth is crumpled
when pushed aside by an impatient guest.

In their hardened layers the sedimentary rocks pre-
serve the evidence of their aquatic origin, the imprints
of ancient plants and the shells of long-dead animals.
These markings make the script readable to the geologist who studies the "record of the rocks," from which
he is able to reconstruct past happenings on our Earth
and in her oceans. Unfortunately the destructive action
of erosion—from temperature variations, frosts, rainfall
and running water—has cut deeply into these records, so
that pages or even whole volumes are missing, making
the work of deciphering the record laborious and its results uncertain.

In the deep ocean, on the other hand, the deposits
have never—or at least very rarely—been disturbed.
They have been formed by an incessant, very slow fall
of minute particles settling from the ocean surface,
many of which are remnants of tiny organisms of the
plankton.[2] Their silica skeletons or calcareous shells
make a large contribution to the carpet spread over the
ocean floor and give indications of the conditions prevailing in the upper water-layers at the time when they
were living. If only the records of the deep could be
thoroughly studied, many obscure chapters in the past
history of our planet would stand revealed to science.

Hitherto, only the very uppermost layers of oceanic
deposits have been accessible to study by means of core-
samplers penetrating a few feet below the surface.
Nevertheless, their study has provided most interesting
results both to oceanographers and to students of sub-

[2] A word derived from the Greek and meaning "drifting."

marine geology. They afford evidence of great catas-
trophes—climatic, volcanic and structural—which have
happened to our planet.

During the Ice Ages the ocean surface was considerably cooler than at present, even near the Equator. The
surface plankton of those times, shedding their tiny
shells over the bottom of the sea, consisted of different
organisms from those of warmer climatic periods. Again,
a local rise or subsidence of the ocean bed, sometimes by
thousands of feet, due to the sudden release of tectonic
forces in the Earth's crust, gave rise to stratified sediments of a peculiar structure. At other times, rains of
ashes from terrific volcanic outbreaks were spread by
the upper winds over thousands of square miles of sea
surface. Settling down to the bottom, these ash rains
have inserted pages by the god of the fires of the under-
world, Vulcan, into the records kept by his rival, the
sea-god Neptune, in the shape of coarse-grained layers
of "pyroclastic" origin, intercalated in the ordinary fine-
grained sediment. (See Fig. 4.)

During the famous *Challenger* Expedition of seventy-
five years ago, 1872-76, which threw open the ocean
depths to research, sounding-tubes were used which
stamped out sediment cores between one and two feet
long from the deposits. The maximum core-length obtained half a century later by the German Atlantic
Expedition with the *Meteor* barely exceeded three feet,
a very moderate advance in fifty years. In the early
1930's, Dr. C. S. Piggot of the Carnegie Institution in
Washington, D.C., invented an ingenious but somewhat
dangerous device, an explosive sampler, which shot the
coring-tube down into the deposit from a kind of submarine gun, discharged automatically on contact with
the bottom. By means of this sampler, a small number of

cores from six to ten feet in length were raised from the bottom of the North Atlantic between Newfoundland and Ireland. In these longer cores American geologists were able to identify four different glacial layers, deposited at various times when the sea surface in those latitudes was cooled by drifting ice-floes and icebergs, the latter broken loose from vast continental ice-caps.

Two different layers of volcanic ash from great eruptions were also discovered in some of the cores. To the uppermost, and consequently youngest, of these ash layers an age of about thirteen thousand years has been attributed. An advance to still greater core-length by this method proved impractical, since the charge of explosives required for overcoming the enormous water pressure prevailing in great depths, and thus for sending the tubular projectile farther down into the bottom, would have involved still greater dangers to the ship and its crew.

During World War II, Swedish oceanographers devoted themselves largely to improving the tools of deep-sea research, especially coring devices, in order to obtain undisturbed sediment columns of still greater length. With these tools we might hope to penetrate much farther back-

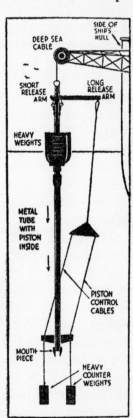

Fig. 1.—Principle of the vacuum core-sampler.

ward in time, that is, to obtain much older "volumes" of the records of the deep. In 1942 the so-called vacuum core-sampler, in which the high water pressure was used for forcing the column of sediment to rise inside a long coring-tube made from fine Swedish steel, was constructed by the author in collaboration with Dr. B. Kullenberg. (See Fig. 1.)

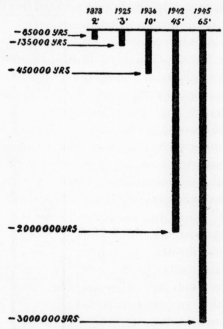

Fig. 2.—Increase in length of cores obtained, with approximate ages, from 1873 to 1945.

With this instrument, an undisturbed core nearly 50 feet long was raised from the bottom of the Gullmar Fiord. Three years later a much improved apparatus, the piston core-sampler of Dr. Kullenberg's devising—in which water pressure is also used—yielded a record core nearly 70 feet long. A core of that length, if taken from the slowly accumulating red clay in the great depths of the Atlantic Ocean, would correspond to a span of time of about three millions years. (See Fig. 2.) This indicates the progress in core-length made since the *Challenger* days. In a similar core taken from the central part of the Pacific Ocean, where the red clay is deposited five to ten times as slowly, the lowest portion should have an age of twenty to thirty millions years.

Another Swedish scientist, Professor W. Weibull, of the famous Bofors Armament Works, assisted us by developing a method for measuring the thickness of the sediment carpet spread over the ocean floor. This method records the echoes from charges exploded at great depths. Strong echoes are thrown back against the upper sediment surface, whereas much fainter and more or less retarded echoes are reflected against the lower surface of the sediment carpet, after the explosive wave has travelled twice through its whole thickness. The velocity of sound in the sediment is higher than that in water, and once it is ascertained, the time lag between the upper and the lower echoes affords a means of calculating the thickness of the sediment carpet down to the reflecting layer. (See Fig. 3.)

In order to test these and other new

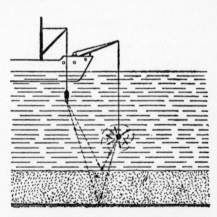

Fig. 3.—Using echoes of explosions at great depths to determine depth of sediment.

tools of research in much greater depths than those found off our Scandinavian coasts, the Swedish Government gave us permission to use the State research ship *Skagerak* for an experimental cruise to the western Mediterranean during April and May of 1946.

Although the *Skagerak* was not properly equipped for work with such heavy gear as the core-samplers required, a number of cores from 20 to 50 feet long were raised by Kullenberg, who directed the sounding operations, from depths between 1000 and 2000 fathoms. In three of these unique cores especially, taken between the Gulf of Naples and Sardinia, a great number of volcanic ash layers were found, probably due to explosive eruptions of Mt. Vesuvius and of neighboring volcanoes in historic and prehistoric times. Fig. 4 gives tentative datings for the more recent of these eruptions, including the terrible outbreak of A.D. 79, when Pompeii and Herculaneum were destroyed. Investigations of the physical and chemical character of these cores, their content of minerals, calcareous shells, of radium and of pollen grains, have yielded results of great interest. Weibull's echo soundings of the carpet of sediment off Algiers in the Tyrrhenian Sea gave very promising results, and the experience gained led to further improvements in his method.

During the last weeks of the cruise, biological investigations, trawlings and dredgings were carried out at great depths between the Strait of Gibraltar and the Josephine Bank far out in the Atlantic. Dr. O. Nybelin, Director of the Natural History Museum in Göteborg, who directed this work, found among the catch three bathypelagic, or deep-sea, fish new to science. (See reproduction of one in Plate 22.)

In Sweden great interest was evoked by the new tech-

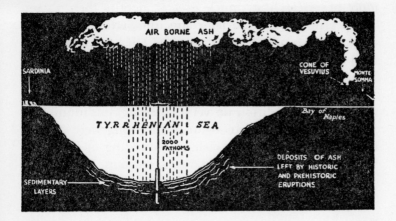

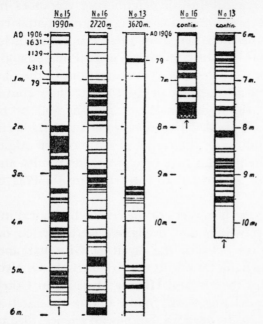

Fig. 4.—Ash zones from the Tyrrhenian Sea.

nique and by the prospects it offered of penetrating deeper into the ocean floor and unravelling its secrets. The large funds required for a Swedish expedition to sail around the world were given by private donors to the Royal Society of Göteborg, and the new training-ship of the Broström combine, the *Albatross,* was lent us for the expedition on very generous conditions.

My dreams were to come true after all.

Chapter 2

PLANNING THE CRUISE

To plan an Earth-circumnavigating deep-sea cruise on the Monaco world map of the ocean depths is a fascinating task. There are so many parts of the ocean floor which offer exciting problems. The deep "trenches" with their incredible depths of from 4000 to nearly 6000 fathoms, the enormous submarine ridges or mountain chains like the Central Atlantic Ridge, which divides the Atlantic Ocean into two separate valleys, the practically unexplored southern parts of the Pacific and the Indian Oceans: these are all tantalizing objectives to the oceanographer.

To us, planning the Swedish Deep-Sea Expedition, the scope had, however, to be limited for technical reasons. The very heavy gear used in coring represented a load on our deep-sea winch which, with increase of depth and of length of the wire rope used, could reach a maximum of about ten tons. This precluded work in the storm-swept waters of the higher latitudes where opportunities for coring operations would necessarily be limited to occasional spells of calm weather. We had, therefore, to keep within the fair-weather region of the globe, *i.e.* to the belt of the equatorial calms, and to avoid as far as possible work in latitudes beyond 30° North and South. Fortunately the ocean floor in the tropics, and especially near the Equator, presents features of special interest, with depths varying between 2000 and 3000 fathoms. Furthermore, it had rarely been followed over long distances by earlier deep-sea expeditions, which have generally crossed it along more or less meridional courses.

Another limitation we had to consider was that of time. The *Albatross* had been lent to us for a cruise of fifteen months' duration, to which must be added three months for fitting her out before the cruise and two months for reconverting her to a combined freighter and training-ship. In the equatorial calms we could not expect to have much use for the sails, but would have to depend largely on the auxiliary diesel engine. With its nominal 600 h.p. it gave the *Albatross* a speed of eight to nine knots—in fair weather. Against a head wind or an adverse swell the speed fell to four knots, or even less. We were advised to base our calculation on an average speed of only seven knots. In order not to exceed the time-limit, we had to avoid making any great detours however tempting they might appear. The course actually followed appears on the map in Fig. 5.

We had originally intended to start with a three-months cruise in the North Atlantic Ocean down to the Equator and, after that, to pass through the Caribbean Sea and make our entry through the Panama Canal into the still vaster field of work offered by the Pacific Ocean. Various difficulties of a technical nature, however, delayed the start from the beginning of March to early July. Had we then followed the original plan, we would

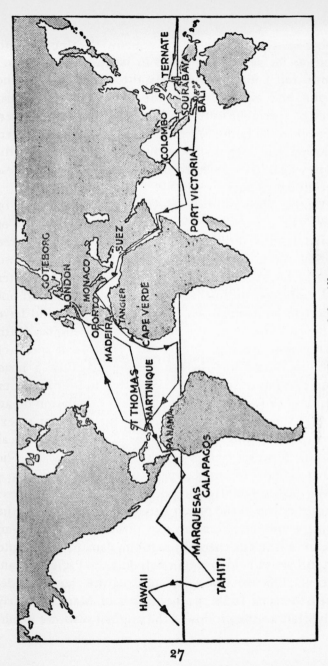

Fig. 5.—Course of the *Albatross*.

have entered the Caribbean at the height of the hurricane season. Later on, in the Indian Ocean, we would have had to battle against the southwest monsoon and the intense surface currents it raises. We were thus obliged to postpone our extensive Atlantic program, taking a short-cut to the West Indian waters, and to hope for a chance of making our planned circuit down to the Equator on the return voyage. This change of plans also made it necessary to postpone the concluding stage of the cruise: biological work in the great depths of the Atlantic Ocean. As it turned out, this delay actually presented decided advantages, especially in the experience gained in handling the great winch and its long wire ropes during coring operations in the two other oceans.

Like the *Challenger* Expedition, we had opportunities of visiting various ocean islands, several of them of great botanical interest. Our Swedish authority on the Pacific island flora, Professor C. Skottsberg, had intended to travel with the expedition from Panama to Hawaii. For various reasons, to our great regret, he had to give up the plan. Instead he delegated to the ship's surgeon, Dr. J. Eriksson—an experienced naturalist and a splendid photographer—the task of making botanical collections on the islands visited. In the Pacific and the Indian Oceans, Eriksson also made a number of hauls with a large ring-net, which caught those fantastic bathypelagic fish and the invertebrate animals which inhabit the intermediate water layers, a few thousand fathoms above the abyssal ocean floor.

But our main purpose was the investigation of the ocean bottom at great depths, its deposits, their interaction with the ocean water, and the thickness of the sediment carpet. Dr. B. Kullenberg, ably assisted by our expedition's mechanic, Mr. A. Jonasson, conducted these complicated operations with consummate skill. In remedying initial troubles with our big winch and other equipment, valuable help was given by the chief engineer of the *Albatross,* Mr. H. Enwall. Our second objective was to measure the thickness of the sediment carpet by the method developed by Professor W. Weibull, who conducted the operations in person during our first Atlantic crossing. During the rest of the cruise, the sediment soundings were carried out by Mr. V. Wenzel, a pupil of our Swedish authority on ionospheric research, Professor O. Rydbeck of Göteborg. Wenzel also seized the opportunity of sounding the ionosphere, a hundred miles or more *over* our heads, by means of short radio waves, for which purpose he had a special set of instruments mounted in one of our laboratories.

The program in physical oceanography comprised a study of the water layers from surface to bottom, their temperature and salinity, their content of dissolved oxygen, of nutrient salts, etc. The cruise afforded excellent opportunities for studying the Equatorial Counter-Current with its complicated dynamics, and the adjacent regions of "divergence" and "convergence," that is, of water masses descending or rising up to the surface from below. This important work was entrusted to Dr. N. Jerlov and Dr. F. Koczy, who made four complete sections across the equatorial current system in the Pacific Ocean and two in the Indian Ocean. In addition, measurements were made of the submarine daylight in different spectral regions, including the ultraviolet, by means of specially constructed instruments, and also of the particles suspended in the water at different depths.

A special feature of our program was the study of the radioactive elements, uranium and radium, present in sea-water and in the deposits. Research extending over many years, partly in Sweden, partly in Vienna, and also, more recently, in the United States, had indicated that radium, continuously replenished by production from its mother element ionium, is present in sediment cores at great depths. These radioactive "time-keepers" afford a means of measuring the age of the different strata of sediment and the rate of deposition. This fortunate circumstance opens a possibility of studying the chronology of the deep-sea sediments, and by these means we may be able to date the records of the deep. For this purpose a water-bottle of special construction, capable of raising large volumes of sea-water (seven gallons at each haul), was included in our equipment.

All these and many other minor details of equipment had to be considered in drawing up the program for the expedition. The Royal Society of Göteborg assigned this task to an organization committee with Governor M. Jacobsson as chairman, Major H. Jacobsson, Mr. T. E. Broström, Professor C. Skottsberg, Dr. O. Nybelin and the author as members, and with Dr. B. Kullenberg as secretary. This committee was also in charge of fitting out the *Albatross* with laboratories, etc. Here we had the great advantage of being able to use all the space otherwise used for cargo.

In the fore- and aft-holds of the ship our heaviest gear was located. The great electric deep-sea winch with its motor and drum for the wire ropes was mounted in the fore-hold, while the diesel electric plant for generating the current for the winch was set up in the aft-hold. Profiting from the experience of earlier expeditions we separated the storage of the long wire rope from the operation of hoisting and lowering it with a full load. The latter function was carried out by two large revolving drums with grooves over which five to seven turns of the wire rope were laid. Thanks to this arrangement and to the excellent quality of the main wire rope from Wright Ropes Co., of Birmingham, the operations both of coring and of trawling at great depths down to a maximum of 4300 fathoms were carried out without any serious mishap. But the control of the wire rope, especially in a rising wind and swell, was often a nerve-racking job for the operators.

Besides cabins for a staff of ten to twelve, and a mess-room, we had on two decks no less than nine laboratories for various purposes, all of which were air-conditioned for work in the tropics. In addition, a large low-temperature room kept at about 40° F. was used for storing the precious sediment cores in an unchanged condition. Compared with earlier expeditions our accommodations were very spacious and proved well adapted to all the different kinds of work we had to carry on. As experience proved, the *Albatross* had been converted into a very efficient floating laboratory and workshop.

Besides the specialists already mentioned, Mr. G. Arrhenius, geologist, was in charge of the operations in the sediment room, assisted by my son, Mr. R. Pettersson. Both Dr. J. Eriksson and, during the concluding Atlantic cruise, Dr. O. Nybelin, in addition to their zoological and botanical work, gave much help with the operations required for extracting the cores, carrying out a preliminary examination, describing them cursorily and packing them hermetically for cold storage. Indeed the spirit of teamwork pervaded the whole scientific and technical staff, everyone willingly lending a hand outside of his own specialty.

The ship was most ably commanded by Captain Nils Krafft and his officers. The crew, including twelve young apprentices, carried out their share of the work with a will and contributed to the spirit of co-operation which characterized the entire enterprise.

PLATE I

GLOBIGERINA BULLOIDES

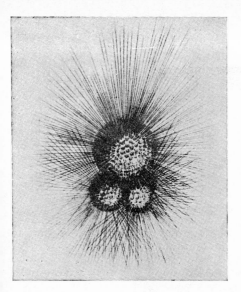

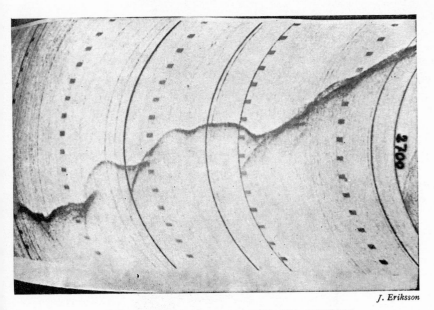

J. Eriksson

THE RISING PROFILE OF THE SEA BOTTOM

PLATE 2

JONASSON MEASURES THE
OBLIQUITY OF THE CABLE

DR. KULLENBERG AT THE CONTROLS
OF THE DEEP-SEA WINCH

Chapter 3

THE START

A deep-sea expedition scheduled to last for fifteen months and equipped with various new instruments is not easy to plan. Our team had been working hard for several years on the planning and preparations, and the concluding months were hectic. All went well, however, and on the 4th of July in the year of grace 1947 everything was ready, all hands were on board and the farewells of wives, children, relatives and creditors were over. It was a fine summer day with a clear sky and a moderate breeze. We slipped our moorings and the snow-white *Albatross*, a stately sight to behold, slowly moved out of the harbor of Göteborg saluted by sirens, flags and waving handkerchiefs—some wet with tears.

We on board were in an elated mood, for our great adventure was just beginning. We had, literally speaking, the whole world before us. The deep ocean bed with its secrets, hidden for millions upon millions of years, was waiting to be explored. There were also enticing prospects of seeing with our own eyes the splendor of the ocean islands, their waving palm trees, their blue lagoons fringed with dazzling white coral beaches. But—

would everything turn out as we hoped? Would our highly complicated gear work to our satisfaction, and make the ocean floor give up its secrets—or would our precious wire ropes snap under the terrific strain, one after the other? Would our long core-samplers stick in an unyielding sediment, forcing us to turn back without any long deep-sea cores to show? Many of our colleagues, as we well knew, had serious doubts that we could achieve what we had set out to do. The whole enterprise was so novel that such doubts were not unwarranted. But everyone, including the skeptics, wished us godspeed, good luck and a happy return.

As early as the second day out, the sea had changed her mood. A hard wind blew from the southwest, and there were low drifting clouds chasing each other above our heads, a sure sign of more wind to come. The *Albatross* started curtseying to the rising swell, a graceful movement to which some on board responded ungraciously. But she was a splendid ship, eminently seaworthy, and she had been trimmed with extra ballast by experts, so that her movements were surprisingly moderate even in a rough sea. Nevertheless, several of our young apprentices were violently sick, while others grew paler and more unsteady on their legs with each new gust of wind. The members of the staff, fortunately, kept their chins up and there was no craving for "Mothersill" or for other popular remedies against what the French politely call *mal de mer*. Our excellent doctor, having no other outlet for his energy, seized the opportunity of giving us various injections against half a dozen mortal maladies encountered in tropical harbors.

All through the Skagerak, the North Sea and the Channel—strewn with melancholy relics of World War II in the shape of masts of ships which had been sunk by mines or torpedoes—the same headwind hampered our progress, reducing our speed from eight knots to six, and from six knots to four or even three. To us who had over 40,000 nautical miles to cover in a bare fifteen months—minus time allotted for work at sea and for refitting in harbors—this crawling rate of progress gave dismal prospects for the future. But even a headwind does not blow forever, and we eventually reached the Bay of Biscay, where, for the first time, we met with depths exceeding 2500 fathoms.

Our entry into these troubled waters, the terror of all passengers subject to seasickness, was greeted by two giants of the deep, a couple of enormous blue whales which, supremely indifferent to our ship, came to close quarters, lustily blowing their spray high up into the air. Other visitors were two carrier-pigeons which alighted on deck in an exhausted condition. Reinvigorated by a square meal and a rest in my cabin, they soon took wing again, carrying their messages to an unknown destination.

Two very pleasant engineers from the Marine Instruments Co., of London, accompanied the expedition from Göteborg to Portugal, in order to test and trim the new recording echo-sounder, which presented a number of highly ingenious features meant to increase its range. They had made a similar trip with the *Skagerak* on her way to the Mediterranean in 1946, when the instrument was still in an experimental stage. They reminded me of a radio message I had proposed, on that occasion, to send to their respected chief in London, Mr. Arthur Hughes, when they were in despair over the unsatisfactory results they first obtained in Biscayan waters: "Bottom of Biscay in unresponsive mood. *Skagerak*'s bottom sore with transmitting. Your two representatives gone overboard looking for missing echoes. Wreaths may be sent to Lisbon. The ways of Providence are unfathomable." The message was not dispatched, but a draft of it still adorns the walls in their office.

To the powerful beam of ultrasonic waves sent out by the new transmitter from the *Albatross* even the Bay of Biscay now responded, giving echoes indicating a depth of 2700 fathoms. This encouraged Kullenberg to start the sounding operations, but when the corer came up its contents were practically nil. Evidently it had hit hard bottom, a most surprising result at this great depth, where one would expect to meet a sediment carpet of considerable thickness. Had we happened by chance to hit a spot where strong bottom currents had scoured the bed-rock beneath free of deposits, or struck a basaltic effusion from a recent submarine eruption? As there were no fragments from the hard bottom sticking in the bit of the corer, there was no answer to these tantalizing questions.

On the following day Weibull exploded one of his charges at a depth of 1400 fathoms, halfway down to the bottom. Echoes, reflected both from the bottom itself and from the water surface above, were distinctly recorded, but there was no trace of deeper echoes such as might have been thrown back against the lower surface of a sediment carpet. The thickness of the latter cannot, therefore, have been more than, say, 10 to 20 fathoms and most probably was nil.

On July 15th we reached Leixoes, harbor of the city of Oporto. We visited this ancient town and sampled the vintages for which it is famous. Afterward we brought on board a small stock of excellent port wine, from which we derived considerable comfort during the cruise. Our English guests left us, satisfied with the

proper functioning of their echo-sounder. Spare parts
for the ship's diesel engine, which had followed us by
air, had duly arrived in Lisbon. Our naive hopes that
they would be released by the Portuguese Customs Office were shattered the following day. The word *mañana,*
which literally means "tomorrow," but which can actually be interpreted as "the day after the day after the
day after tomorrow, if it pleases God," is the national
proverb in Portugal. It serves as an iron curtain against
all northwest European hustle, which is altogether futile
in the easy-going South. We had to wait for three weary
days in Leixoes before our indispensable parcel was de-
livered into our hands by a perfect example of official
sluggishness.

However, our forced inactivity was used for making a
trip by car to the mountainous north, visiting the famous shrine of Vania de Castelo. We were taken to
remarkable ruins perched on the top of a steep hill,
from which there was a glorious view up and down the
coast. The ruins were said to be remnants of a long-
vanished pre-Phoenician culture, and to have the ma-
ture age of about six thousand years. Being on the
lookout for sediments millions of years old, we were
not overly impressed.

Our return journey to Oporto was enlivened by the
reckless speed at which our chauffeur drove us along
precipices and around hairpin bends, the only activity,
besides talking, which the Southerners carry on at top
speed. We suggested that he should apply for a transfer
to the Customs Office, where he might inject some pep.

According to our itinerary, we should have set course
W.S.W. from Leixoes, heading straight for the West
Indies and Martinique, where Fort-de-France was our
next port of call. But at the first sounding taken in the

Bay of Biscay, our big winch had already displayed disquieting symptoms of running warm. On a close inspection, our chief engineer found that the base on which the winch was mounted had given way slightly on one side, only by a fraction of an inch but sufficient to increase seriously the friction in the bearings of the large drums. It was necessary to correct this, and as that could be done only in the calm water of a harbor, we decided to run down to Funchal on Madeira before crossing the Atlantic Ocean. The very idea of spending weeks in a Portuguese harbor, trying to rouse the officials out of their *mañana* torpor, made us shudder.

Chapter 4

THE EMERALD OF THE
ATLANTIC OCEAN

Scanning the Monaco chart of the Atlantic Ocean depths, one's attention is drawn to the region lying to the west and southwest of the Strait of Gibraltar, between the parallels N. 30° and N. 37°. Here is a strange submarine "landscape." Enormous mountains run up from depths exceeding 14,000 feet, with their flat summits only a few hundred feet beneath the ocean surface. Their horizontal extent is so limited that it took years of painstaking labor, by means of mechanical sounding instruments, to locate them. Because of their slimness, they had slipped through the wide-meshed net of earlier hydrographic surveys. Cable-laying operations helped to reveal their presence.

A newly-laid submarine telegraph cable between Lisbon and Madeira soon broke down and had to be repaired—a very tedious operation. A few months later another break occurred at almost the same spot, where the great depth would not have led one to suspect any obstacle endangering a cable. Then, after a detailed study of the depths near the critical spot, the obstacle, or rather pinnacle, which had caused the damage was discovered—the steep, almost precipitous slopes of the Seine Bank, on which the cable had become strained beyond its critical point. Further investigations undertaken on a more extensive scale revealed three more of these skyscrapers of the deep: the Josephine Bank, the Gettysburg Bank, and the Coral Patch. Rising at angles which rival those of many lofty peaks in the Alps or in the Andes, these submarine alpine needles lift their crests sufficiently near the surface for a ship to anchor there, right in the open ocean.

There can be no doubt about the origin of these famous banks. In the Indian Ocean, and still more in the Pacific, such mementos of volcanic forces are quite common. Most of them, however, are crowned with diadems of snow-white coral, forming the atolls, reefs and lagoons of the South Seas. In the Atlantic Ocean extensive coral growth is much rarer, especially along the eastern boundary. Here the basaltic rocks, levelled by wave action at a time when the sea surface was lower than at present, are naked, swept clear of all sediment by the scouring action of tidal currents.

During our experimental cruise with the *Skagerak* in the preceding year, we had devoted a couple of days to echo-soundings and biological investigations of the Josephine Bank, first discovered in 1883 by a Swedish man-of-war of the same name. With the *Albatross* we now passed over the Seine Bank, where our echo-sounder drew a picturesque contour. But Weibull's attempt to investigate the structure of the bank by means of exploding depth-charges yielded no positive results.

The great volcanic eruptions have resulted not only in submarine mountains but have also given rise to lovely islands of which that of Madeira is by far the most famous. Her enchanted gardens, filled with flowers, shrubs and trees belonging both to the temperate and to the subtropical zones, form a mantle of brilliant verdure for this wonderful "daughter of the deep sea," the "Emerald of the Atlantic." To us on board the *Albatross,* approaching the island on an early summer morning, she was a roseate dream floating on a sea of lapis lazuli.

For several hours our echo-sounder had been recording a series of steeply rising and falling curves, representing submerged rivers of ancient lava, separated by deep chasms. Behind us we had the Seine Bank, an island stillborn, with its wave-worn crest submerged beneath a hundred fathoms of ocean water, whereas Madeira carries her lofty pinnacles to heights of more than 6000 feet above the ocean out of which she was born.

> *A day-born dream of divine unreason,*
> *A marvel moulded of sleep—no more?*

—as Swinburne sings in his exquisite poem, "A Swimmer's Dream." When did the catastrophe occur which gave birth to Madeira, making volcanic cones shoot up from the abyss, emitting enormous masses of red-hot lava over the ocean floor? One or two scores of million years ago, say the geologists, who have as little respect for large numbers as have astronomers—or modern financiers. But long after that remote time the strange forces remained at work, piling up the lovely island, making her still more picturesque by adding new volcanic cones to those of earlier dates. Indeed several of them are, geologically speaking, of quite recent origin. The very youngest among them may have been forged after the dawn of Western civilization.

This possibility raises the old and ever-renewed question: "What about Plato's Lost Atlantis?" The wonderful kingdom of the deep, ruled by ten kings, descendants of Poseidon—the great island kingdom from which the first attempt was made to subjugate Europe, and which disappeared beneath the waves during a day and night of terrible catastrophe? Is this only "a day-born dream of divine unreason"? Or are there real facts behind the immortal tale, as related in the two Platonic "Dialogues," *Timaeus* and *Critias?*

Every argument advanced so far in defense of the reality of the fabulous submerged island kingdom has been shattered by critical research. No organized civilization existed, either outside or within the "Pillars of Hercules" more than a hundred centuries ago, as Plato's romance will have it. But perhaps an oral tradition of great floods due to volcanic action, submerging the shores of the northwest African coast and the southwest European coast may have survived until Hellenic times and may form the nucleus about which Plato has spun his golden tale. Who knows? A wise man has said: "One has to be skeptical even of one's own skepticism."

The snow-white hull of the *Albatross*, with her four towering masts, made a fine picture in every harbor we visited. Perhaps never had she appeared to greater advantage than here, with the amphitheater of emerald-green slopes as a background, and behind them the rose-colored hills rising up toward a sapphire-blue sky. Our friends ashore, who gave us a hearty reception, expressed their admiration for this most beautiful expedition ship, the first for many years to visit Funchal. We had renowned predecessors. Here the greatest explorer of modern times, Captain James Cook, made a landing on his last and most famous expedition to the Pacific Ocean, in the year 1772. A tulip tree which he then planted in one of the gardens was shown to us as a venerable relic. H.M.S. *Challenger* touched at Funchal, both when outward bound in 1873 and on the return voyage in 1876. Half a century later, the Danish expedition ship *Dana* also visited Funchal. Its leader was the great biologist, Dr. Johannes Schmidt, who solved the mystery of the migrations and the propagation of the common eel. These, as well as many other expeditions, had been given the same cordial reception by hospitable Funchal as we enjoyed.

We were taken to the merchant house of Blandy, which handled all matters pertaining to our ship and to the formalities of our call. Our visit was extended to their wine cellar, one of the oldest in Funchal. We were initiated into the making and the treatment of the noble Madeira wine, beloved by the English as early as the Elizabethan era. Shakespeare, for instance, in the First Part of *King Henry IV*, writes: "What says Sir John Sack-and-Sugar? Jack, how agrees the devil and thee about thy soul, that thou soldest him on Good Friday last, for a cup of Madeira, and a cold capon's leg?" We were not offered any capon's leg by our friendly tempter, but the very old wines he served us were a comfort to the soul. We started with bottled sunshine, a venerable Solera reserve of 1792, worthy of the palate of the Prince Regent himself. We proceeded to a rare Bual of 1808, and then to an exquisite Bual Solera of 1826. In a most agreeable way we passed through the first half of the last century, until the terrible year of 1852, when the vineyards of the island were all but completely laid waste by a fungus blight, known by the name of *Oidium Tuckerii*. With the aid of sulphur, the blight was checked and the vineyards were replanted, but not for long. In 1873 an insect pest, *Phylloxera vastatrix,* which settled on the roots of the vines, sapped their life-blood and killed them outright. The vine culture was resuscitated for the second time by means of imported American vines resistant to *Phylloxera.* But the quality of the wine was poor, until, by grafting shoots from surviving Verdelho vines on to the imported stocks, grapes of quality and resistance were obtained and the wine industry survived.

At present, the wine trade is suffering from other ailments. The exchange restrictions make it well-nigh impossible, both for the English and for Swedes—the chief consumers of the Madeira wines of today—to buy the quantities normally consumed.

Another mainstay of the lovely island was the tourist traffic, which inevitably suffers from the same restrictions. Even the proverbially wealthy English have difficulties in raising the *escudos* required for a winter in Madeira. Scandinavians, for the same reason, also fail to go there. Americans, strange to say, do not seem to have taken to this delightful resort. The big hotels, as well as the dealers in the diverse handicraft products of the island, such as baskets, woodwork, Madeira lace and exquisite 'embroidery, are hard hit by the ebbing of the tourist stream. To those who know the island, this seems a pity, since a more alluring refuge from the rain, the snow and the fog of the sunless northern autumn and early winter cannot be imagined. Thanks to the surrounding ocean, the seasons are retarded, the warmest months being September and October. As early as December strawberries are ripe and public parks, as well as private gardens, are resplendent with multicolored flowers.

We were fortunate in meeting one of Madeira's most distinguished men of science, Mr. Walter Grabham, who gave much time to us, showing us the sights of his beloved island. After many years of active service as geologist to the Sudan Government, Mr. Grabham retired to Funchal where he was born. His father, Dr. M. Grabham, was well known for his natural history studies of Madeira; he died in 1935 at the great age of ninety-five. Mr. Grabham is a leading authority on the geology and the plants of the island. His mother, *née* Blandy, was the sister of Lady Kelvin, married to the then Sir William Thomson, who had made her acquaintance on one of his ocean cruises. To us, physicists of a later generation, it gave a peculiar thrill to hear Mr. Grabham speak of our demi-god, Lord Kelvin, greatest of all nineteenth-century physicists, as "Uncle Willy." He also showed us, in the harbor of Funchal, the remnants of the first tidal gauge which Lord Kelvin had built there in order to pursue his pioneer work on the ocean tides. It was in Mr. Grabham's delightful old garden that we saw the tulip tree planted by Captain Cook, and also made the acquaintance of the famous dragon tree, indigenous to Madeira and the Canary Islands.

We also had the privilege of visiting a still more magnificent garden, high up in the hills, belonging to the present head of the house of Blandy. Nearly two centuries ago, the founder of the house saved this unique botanical garden, planted by an eccentric Portuguese count, from being cut down by its owner, who had ruined himself by living not wisely but too well. It is said to contain no less than eight hundred different trees from South America, South Africa, The Himalaya, etc., many of them of giant growth. The number of Camellia bushes—unfortunately not in flower at the time of our visit—runs into tens of thousands. Our eyes were delighted by acres upon acres of agapanthus, blue and white, of which Mrs. Blandy presented us with two enormous bunches. She also gave us a basket full of delicious plums, before we were driven back in a luxurious car down the steep road leading to Funchal.

Before leaving the enchanted garden, we were taken into an old rococo building, now used for storing fruit, where the spendthrift count had lived. Exquisite decorations were still visible on the walls. One could well imagine them as a background for stately minuets and graceful gavottes, trod to Couperin's music by the gay guests of an Almaviva, who wasted his substance on wine, women and song.

One of the many sights of Funchal is its new market, with an overwhelming abundance of flowers, fruits and berries—from strawberries and aromatic silver bananas to grapes, which were just then coming in. To us strangers from the frugal North, the prices seemed incredibly low. In the adjacent fish-market there was a deafening noise from swarthy fish-vendors, loudly crying out their wares. Large chunks of blood-red tunnies, the "oxen of the sea," were cut up for sale, and we were also offered strange-looking inhabitants of the great depths, like the ugly but palatable scabbard fish. It somewhat resembles an eel, but has an enormous mouth, and bears a rather terrifying pattern of black and white. The upwelling waters around the island make these and other rarities of the great deep accessible to the nets and hooks of the fisher-folk.

Before we left Funchal with our big winch readjusted, our Captain invited some of our Madeira friends for a real Swedish dinner on board. Our ice-cold beer and the Swedish *Schnapps,* drunk with hors-d'oeuvres to melodious drinking songs, were highly appreciated by our guests. In parting, Mr. Grabham gave me a unique present, a bottle of old Madeira which had been given to the *Challenger* Expedition on their first visit to Funchal, and was carried around the world on their cruise. A few of the remaining bottles had been returned to the donors on the second visit, in memory of the cruise. It was given to me on the express condition that it was not to be consumed before it had been a second time around the world, on the *Albatross*, a condition which was faithfully observed.[1]

With feelings of deep gratitude, mingled with regret at leaving this wonderful island and the charming friends we had found there, we set out to continue our voyage. A gentle trade wind filled our sails. Brilliant sunshine played over the waves by day, and silvery moonlight by night, as we drew farther away from Europe, heading for another jewel of the Atlantic Ocean, the pearl of the West Indies, Martinique.

[1] The *Challenger* Madeira was consumed during our visit to London in September 1948. Among the guests who shared the bottle were two British admirals, the Deputy Master of Trinity House, the Chief of the Discovery Department of the Colonial Office, and the Director of the Swedish Institute in London, worthy recipients of the unique wine, which had twice made its world tour, first with H.M.S. *Challenger*, and three-quarters of a century later with the *Albatross*.

Chapter 5

CROSSING THE ATLANTIC OCEAN

It is a wonderfully clear morning far out on the Atlantic Ocean. Straight ahead the full moon is sinking into the sea, and the silver bridge it spreads before us is rapidly waning before the first rays from the sun rising in our wake. Suddenly, just under the bows of the *Albatross,* swarms of flying fish, the glittering dragonflies of the tropical sea, are scared out of the water by that strange giant fish which seems to pursue them. They are masters of soaring flight, these beautiful creatures. Time after time they barely touch the surface, gathering impetus for continued flight by means of their rapidly vibrating tail fins.

Since 2 A.M. I have been watching the recording echo-sounder, magically drawing the profile of the ocean bottom many thousands of feet below our keel. Far down in the hull of the ship there is a bundle of nickel plates vibrating 10,000 times per second under the influence of a strong magnetic field varying with the same frequency. Short pulses of these ultrasonic waves, concentrated downward by a reflector behind the vibrator, are passing out into the water through a thin membrane of

48

PLATE 3

THE LONG CORING TUBE
PREPARED FOR LOWER-
ING

J. Eriksson

THE CORER IN DESCENT

PLATE 4

TAKING THE CORER ON
BOARD

J. Eriksson

KULLENBERG AND JONASSON
TAKING OUT A CORE

J. Eriksson

PUSHING OUT THE INNER TUBE

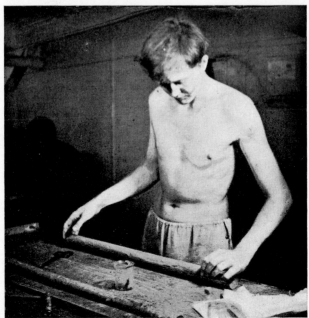

J. Eriksson

ARRHENIUS STUDYING THE CONTENTS OF THE CORER

PLATE 5

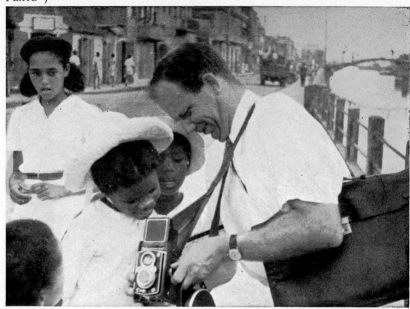

R. Pettersson

DR. ERICSSON WITH PHOTO-MINDED NEGRO CHILDREN

MONT PELEE   *R. Pettersson*

steel. Their echo from the sea floor returns to the ship and enters through another steel membrane, reaching an electric receiver. From there the ultrasonic waves, transformed into electric impulses, are conducted to the echo-graph in the laboratory. The moments of the emission and of the reception of each pulse are recorded on a chemically-treated strip of paper slowly rotated by an electric motor. Thus, from a sequence of small points, a curve appears which, on a reduced scale, shows how the bottom rises and falls along the course we are following.

Since the velocity of sound waves in water is about 5000 feet per second, only a few seconds are required for the pulses emitted to reach the ocean bed and be reflected back to our receiver. Multiplying the "echo-time" by 5000, therefore, gives the total distance which the ultrasonic impulses have traversed, which is twice the actual depth. The earlier "mechanical" sounding technique—using a lead lowered to the bottom, the length of its steel wire giving a measure of the depth—took several hours to make a single sounding at a depth of, say, 3000 fathoms. With no physical contact, the echo-graph achieves the same purpose in a fraction of a minute and is, moreover, capable of repeating the sounding continuously at intervals of a few seconds.

It is most fascinating to watch the ocean bottom drawing its own profile by means of this marvel of engineering while our ship pursues its course at a speed of eight to nine knots. Using the highest sensitivity afforded by our echo-graph, we can note changes in depth as small as one to two fathoms. Yet even this splendid instrument has its limitations. With a contrary wind or swell, air bubbles are apt to get below the bottom of the ship, dissipating the energy of the ultrasonic beam and making the echo-grams indistinct or even illegible. Fortunately, we run before the wind for most of the time on our westerly course and the swell is moderate, so that the depth records are generally clear.

A few decades ago, when only a sparse net of mechanical soundings was available, one had the general impression that the deep-sea floor was a gigantic plain and that its depth varied only very little over great distances. This view is proved erroneous by a look at our echo-grams taken between Madeira and Martinique. The bottom profile rises or falls quite often by "steps," a mile or two across and tens if not hundreds of fathoms high. This gives the impression of passing across what land geologists call scarps. In other places the ocean floor is covered with small hills or hummocks, so that the profile drawn is not simple but dissolves into stars made by intersecting lines.

This remarkable ruggedness of the deep ocean floor is of interest from a structural or "morphological" point of view. It also presents serious complications in our work, especially with the long and rather fragile core-samplers. When lowered against a steep slope on the bottom, they may topple over and become bent or even broken. Also, in measuring the thickness of the sediment carpet by Weibull's method of exploding depth-charges, the multiple echoes from the explosion thrown back from the hills and hummocks on the sea floor may often obscure the fainter echoes reflected by deep interfaces within the sediment, or by the surface of the rock-bed beneath it.

Hence the records of the echo-sounder must be consulted before the ship is laid-to for work, so as to avoid areas where the profile is not sufficiently smooth. Where a reasonably smooth sea *is* found, however, operations may begin. The ship is headed into the wind and kept immobile by the engine. The long corer is lifted from its horizontal position along the bulwark on the upper deck and brought forward to the deep-sea winch. This is set in motion, lowering the corer rapidly to the bottom after the necessary number of extra weights have been added. At the last moment, before sending the corer down, the release is made ready so that it will automatically go into action the moment the sea floor is reached. This is the critical moment, when the utmost care is required on the part of the man directing the coring operation, so that the big winch can be stopped dead just as the reduced strain on the dynamometer over which the wire is running out indicates that the release has been set into operation. In a few seconds the entire length of the coring-tube, which may be varied according to the weather, the depth and bottom conditions (from 20 to 60 feet or even more), has been plunged into the sediment. The piston inside remains stationary in contact with the sediment, while the coring-tube descends, forcing a column of sediment to rise upward, filling the thin lining-tubes inside the external heavy steel tube. Then the winch is set to raise the load. After the resistance of the corer sticking in the surrounding sediment has been overcome, the instrument with its precious content can be raised to the surface and put along the bulwark on the upper deck. The sections of lining-tubes, each 28 inches long, are pushed out of the steel tube and brought down into the sediment laboratory. There the deposit is examined and carefully packed.

Thanks to the excellent technique developed by Dr. Kullenberg, an entire coring operation down to a depth of 3000 fathoms could, under favorable conditions, be carried out in a little more than three hours. The scrutiny of the cores conducted by our geologist, Dr. G. Arrhenius, with the ship's doctor as chief helper, took a couple of hours. Finally, packing the core sections in plastic, and enclosing them in aluminum tubes with the residual space filled up with molten paraffin, making them ready for cool storage, took another couple of hours. Because of this time element, we did not often raise more than one or two cores per day from great depths. Nearer the coastline and in shallower depths, especially in the Mediterranean, the number was occasionally increased to three or even four.

After concluding a coring operation, the depth-charges were made ready and the hydrophones by which the different echoes were recorded—either by photographic registering on an oscillograph or by wire-recorder—were hung over the side of the ship. Generally two depth-charges were dropped, one for explosion in moderate depths, 300 to 1400 fathoms, and one for depths of 2500 up to 3500 fathoms. By pressing an ear to the bulwark, one could feel the thud from the explosions which occurred several minutes after the charges had been dropped. The fainter echoes, thrown back by deeper reflecting surfaces in the sediment, were discernible only by means of the recording instruments. The very deepest echoes detected by Weibull during our first Atlantic crossing indicated a reflecting surface some 12,000 feet below the bottom itself. If we assume the whole of the sediment there to be identical with the red clay found in the upper layers, and allow a rate of accumulation of one-fourth inch per thousand years, the total time of accumulation would be some five hundred million years. If we also take into account the compacting effect in the lower layers of sediment, the total time of deposition must be increased considerably.

This result is rather startling; it implies a striking contradiction to the much debated theory of continental

Fig. 6.—Simplified bathymetric chart
of the Atlantic Ocean.

drift, expounded by the Austrian geophysicist Wegener. According to him, the Atlantic Ocean is of relatively late origin, being formed about seventy million years ago, at which time the two Americas drifted away from the Old World. Our results showed, however, that at least that part of the Atlantic Ocean where Weibull found his peak value for the thickness of sediment must be many times older than the age ascribed to it by Wegener.

A simplified bathymetric chart of the Atlantic Ocean is reproduced in Fig. 6, with the depth-line for 4000 meters (about 2200 fathoms) indicated. This contour is seen to enclose a remarkable submarine mountain chain, the "Central Atlantic Ridge," stretching from far north of the Azores down to the latitude of Cape Horn. This ridge separates the deep Atlantic basin into two "Atlantic Valleys" with depths exceeding 2500 fathoms. A transverse submarine ridge appears to stretch almost at right angles to the Ridge, from Tristan da Cunha toward Walvis Bay on the coast of southwest Africa. It serves as a submarine dike, obstructing the passage of the ice-cold Antarctic bottom water from the south into the eastern Atlantic Valley.

Should the pessimistic views of certain geologists be realized—that a progressive desiccation of our planet will lead to a gradual sinking of the ocean surface—a mid-Atlantic continent, separating *two* Atlantic Oceans from each other, will ultimately emerge above the falling sea surface. To what complications in international politics the ownership of this new continent may lead must be left to the imagination.

According to Wegener, the Central Atlantic Ridge is a kind of "birth scar" left behind on the ocean floor when the Old and the New Worlds drifted apart. However, geological evidence found in the last thirty years indicates that the Ridge is probably built up by extensive submarine volcanic action, *i.e.* by molten magma

from deeper layers in the crust being extruded through
an enormously long fissure in the bed of the Atlantic.
The fact that the few mid-oceanic islands of the Atlantic, which rise up from the Ridge, carry active or extinct
volcanoes certainly favors this explanation. Other examples of the important part submarine volcanism must
have played in the development of the two other oceans
will be seen in the following pages.

Some results obtained by our splendid echo-graphs
are of general interest. We were unable to find any confirmation of the existence of the so-called "Fosse de
Monaco" with a depth of more than 3400 fathoms in
lat. 30°55′N., long. 25°25′W.; we found the depth there
to be 250 fathoms less. On the other hand, a still greater,
hitherto apparently unrecorded, depth of over 3500
fathoms was encountered farther to the southwest in lat.
25°10′N., long. 36°30′W. When we passed across the
Central Atlantic Ridge, our echo-graph indicated an
unrecorded minimum depth of not quite 800 fathoms in
lat. 23°00′N., long. 45°11′W. The Admiralty charts have
no similar depth in the vicinity, where 1300 fathoms appears as the minimum.

Here we seem to have hit on the highest point of the
Central Ridge between St. Paul's Rocks and the Azores.
In the event of a progressive sinking of the ocean surface, as has been suggested, this point would be the first
to protrude. Modesty forbids us to suggest that it should
in that remote time be called "Albatross Island."

The color of the sediment cores taken during this
cruise varied from the chocolate brown of the red clay
characteristic of great depths to the nearly white shades
of calcareous sediment, the "globigerina ooze," characteristic of moderate depths near the Central Ridge. On
its western side, however, in greater depths traversed

before we reached the West Indies, the color of the sediment again reverted to chocolate brown, indicating a scarcity of lime.

Being anxious to pass through the Caribbean Sea before the height of the hurricane season, we had to cut short our program of work during the first Atlantic crossing. We consoled ourselves with the prospect of devoting more time to that part of the ocean on our return voyage, and therefore with a clear conscience headed for Martinique.

Chapter 6

IN THE HURRICANE REGION

Like a garland of tropical flowers set in an azure sea, the West Indian islands form a barricade against the Atlantic Ocean. Their apparent peacefulness is deceptive, for they are frequently disturbed by demoniac forces. The mighty fold of the Earth's crust which supports the Antilles is under a terrific strain, a strain which often becomes manifest through destructive earthquakes or volcanic eruptions. Measurements of the gravitational force made in submerged submarines by a method we owe to the Dutch scientist Vening-Meinez prove that these forces have large local variations from their normal value, both to the positive and to the negative side. Such anomalies give a foreboding of still greater disturbance in the future. Some geologists assert that the accumulation of deposits in the deep downward fold running parallel to the island-festoon is heaping up material for an unborn mountain chain predestined to be raised high above the ocean surface, just as the European Alps were raised thirty to sixty million years ago. The same hypothesis has been propounded also with regard to a similar deep trough encircling the East

Indian islands. Perhaps the paroxysms which occasionally shake the very foundations of both these vast archi-
pelagos are early forerunners of the birth-pains of a
tremendous mountain-building process, which will
shake the world millions of years after our time.

Quite a different kind of catastrophe is that caused by
the intensely concentrated atmospheric disturbances
sweeping over the islands—tropical storms or hurricanes.
Late summer and early autumn is the high season of
these dancing dervishes of the air, which we are anxious
to avoid. Hence the timing of our itinerary aiming at a
safe passage through the Caribbean Sea. The *Albatross*
is a sturdy ship capable of weathering a tropical storm.
But the tumultuous waves accompanying such a storm
and creating a powerful ocean-swell hundreds of miles
from the storm center would, for several days, make all
work on board impossible. So we had to push ahead,
strictly limiting our work en route, no matter how
tempting an investigation of the deep basins we were
passing appeared to us.

Approaching Martinique from the northeast, one is
struck by the multitude of volcanic cones jutting up
from the shore. They rise highest in the north with the
sinister peak of Mt. Pelée, the cause of a terrific holo-
caust in May 1902. The top of the volcano was blown
off, a rift in its side opened, and a blast of hot magmatic
gas—a *nuée ardente* as the French say—swept down the
slopes, annihilating all life in its way. The flourishing
city of St. Pierre at its foot was totally destroyed and its
28,000 inhabitants were killed in the course of a few
minutes.

Proceeding southward along the west coast of the
island, one finds the contours tamer until the idyllic
harbor of Fort-de-France is reached. Here our American

guest, Dr. Phleger of the Scripps Oceanographic Institute in La Jolla—who was to accompany us across the Caribbean—was waiting for us. He is a specialist on *foraminifera*—plankton living in the tropical and subtropical ocean surface and spreading their tiny calcareous shells in enormous numbers over the ocean floor. Phleger was given the highest priority by the U.S. Navy for his flying tour to Martinique in order to join the *Albatross* cruise. His host in Fort-de-France, the U.S. Consul, Mr. Hunt, also took us under his wing. Mr. and Mrs. Hunt received us in their home with the hospitality shown by all American and British officials we met during our expedition.

To us northerners, the splendor of tropical vegetation is almost overwhelming. Then, too, there is the great variety of human beings, the products of centuries of interracial crossing. Every shade of color from *café au lait* to black is represented, with a decided predominance of the darker shades. Europeans are relatively scarce in the streets of Fort-de-France. In spite of apparent poverty, the native population wear grins of friendliness and contentment. Beggars are fewer and far less aggressive than those one meets in the south of Europe.

We were invited to dine with the Hunts, and were treated to a variety of local delicacies. Afterward, in the cool of the evening in their spacious garden, there was musical entertainment—Swedish folk songs and Tahitian chants sung by a French naval officer and his wife who had spent some years in Papeete. These were interspersed with American college songs. The accompaniment, by an orchestra of tropical insects hidden in the surrounding trees and bushes, sometimes rose to a deafening *fortissimo*.

The season of the notorious tropical storms was just

beginning. They are most frequent at the end of August, in September, and at the beginning of October. For the West Indian islands they are a terrible scourge. According to statistics extending over more than two hundred years, Martinique has been struck between eight and ten times in each century. During the hours when the atmospheric madness is at its height, damage is wrought amounting to many millions of dollars. Houses, factories and churches collapse, and the growing crops of corn and sugar-cane are destroyed, causing famine for men and cattle. Thousands of human lives are sometimes lost.

Modern meteorological research has located the origin of the West Indian cyclones on the borderline between the equatorial calm and the trade winds. In a similar way the miniature cyclones of Scandinavia, the *trombs,* are generated along the borderline between two air-currents of opposite direction. Once started, the "dancing dervishes" of the tropics follow a curved path, at first to the west, then turning to the north, sometimes even to the northeast. The speed at which they travel is much lower than the wind velocity at the center, which may exceed a hundred miles per hour.

There are many signs giving warning of the approach of a tropical storm; a veil of thin cirrus clouds spreading over the sky, the lower clouds travelling at high speed, a sudden drop of the barometer, and, especially with slowly travelling hurricanes, a high swell coming from the direction of the storm center. Nowadays, thanks to radar, it is possible to view from a considerable distance the intense water condensation which occurs. Intrepid air pilots of the U.S. Navy have repeatedly flown their planes right through the atmospheric vortex and, in spite of a fierce knocking about by blasts and counterblasts, have made valuable observations on the structure of the air masses gyrating around the center of the storm. During the hurricane season a close watch is kept over the breeding-ground of the storms. Once on the move, their probable path is plotted and radioed to a number of meteorological stations, warning the inhabitants of approaching disaster.

Another kind of destructive force which from time to time threatens the peace of the Antilles is subterranean in source. The earliest eruption of Mt. Pelée on record was that of 1792, repeated, after more than half a century of repose, in 1851. After another respite of fifty years came the devastating outbreak of 1902 already mentioned. The year 1902 was critical also for other volcanoes in the Central American region. On April 17th the volcano Quetzaltenango in Guatemala had a violent eruption which coincided with a minor outbreak of Mt. Pelée, a forerunner of the catastrophe on May 8th. On the preceding day, the Soufrière on the island of St. Vincent had gone into action, and on May 10th Izalco in San Salvador broke into eruption. There are many other examples of similar interconnection between volcanoes situated in the same region.

We seized the opportunity of our visit to Fort-de-France to make an excursion on Mt. Pelée. Through a landscape where wild volcanic rocks provided a somber background for lovely tropical vegetation, with scarlet hibiscus and lily-white *fleurs soleil,* we were taken by car toward the volcano. When the radiators of the cars began to boil on the steep grade, our Negro chauffeurs refused to take us farther and we had to continue our ascent toward the crater on foot. Unfortunately its summit was lost in a dense fog, which made most of us give up climbing to the top. On a clear day the view from the crater rim must be magnificent.

Lovely and alluring is the Pearl of the Antilles, as lovely as its most famous daughter, Napoleon's Empress Josephine. A prolonged stay in its warm, moist air is bound to have a deteriorating effect on men from the north. It was in fact with relief that we headed westward from hospitable Fort-de-France, with its venerable fortress.

The bottom of the Caribbean Sea is a tempting field of work for students of the deep sea. Its contour is most varied. Deep troughs alternate with submarine ridges, and the sediments carpeting the underlying rock-bed are most interesting. We should have loved to criss-cross over this lunar seascape, studying the bottom profile with our echo-graph, measuring the sediment carpet with our exploding depth-charges, and raising long cores from depths almost untouched by science. However, we still had three oceans to investigate within the limited time at our disposal, and therefore had to hurry on toward Panama and the great Pacific beyond it.

Our American guest, Dr. Phleger, was intent on examining the small *foraminifera* germinating in the surface waters, and also their tiny calcareous shells on the bottom. He had brought on board an ingenious set of tow-nets, which could be attached to our instrument line, for sampling the minute plankton organisms at different depths. By far the greatest number of the *foraminifera* are pelagic, *i.e.* they drift along with the currents in the upper layers, whereas a much smaller number prefer a more sedate existence as *benthos*, living on the bottom.

The pelagic *foraminifera* in which we were mainly interested comprise well over a score of different species, recognizable by the characteristic shapes of their shells. Some of them, such as *Globorotalia meinardii*, are sensitive to cold and are therefore confined to the warm surface water of tropical seas, whereas others are more hardy, like the dominant species *Globigerina bulloides*, and are able to spread to higher latitudes where the surface is cooler.

Geology teaches us that after untold millions of years of warm climate, when polar ice-caps were absent, a deterioration of climate occurred at the end of the Tertiary Age. During the past million years of the Earth's history—the Quaternary Age—the climate of the world became so severe for long spells that vast masses of inland ice spread over the continents in the higher latitudes. The present ice-caps over Greenland and the Antarctic are much reduced remnants of the ice ages. The cooling influence of the vast inland ice and of the Arctic and Antarctic sea ice reduced the surface temperature of the ocean down to the Equator and severely restricted its population of heat-loving *foraminifera*. During intervals of warmer climate, the so-called "interglacials," they again increased in number. The relative abundance or scarcity of their shells at different levels of the sediment cores therefore represents a kind of temperature record of the Quaternary Age, which can be deciphered by an analysis of the calcareous shells.

Through a biological analysis of the relatively short sediment cores raised from the bottom of the equatorial Atlantic Ocean by the *Meteor* Expedition, the German specialist Professor W. Schott discovered a level about ten inches below the sediment surface where the warm water forms, *Globorotalia meinardii*, became very scarce. At a somewhat deeper level this form again turned up. Schott inferred that the upper limit marked the end of the last glaciation, some twenty thousand years ago, and that the lower limit corresponded to the end of the preceding interglacial period. Similar results have since been obtained by other workers, affording a means for linking submarine geochronology with that evolved for the continents by glaciologists.

Dr. Phleger had already done us the great service of analyzing cores raised in 1946 from the depths of the Tyrrhenian Sea by the *Skagerak*. He had also found there unmistakable signs of climatic variations affecting the composition of the *foraminifera* assemblage. He now had an opportunity of sampling our longest core from the Caribbean Sea, raised from a depth of 2700 fathoms, samples of which he took back for analysis to the Scripps Institute of Oceanography at La Jolla. Before the *Albatross* had returned from her cruise around the world, Phleger had results ready for publication. A summary is reproduced in Fig. 7.

The graph shows how warm and cold periods, indicated by the shells of *foraminifera,* varied with the distance below the sediment surface (given in centimeters at the left-hand side of the graph). The variations found are highly significant, and show cold periods (shaded in the graph) corresponding to the four main periods of glaciation over North America as set out in the right-hand side of the graph. This latter addition to the diagram is the work of an eminent English specialist on *foraminifera* and their relation to climate, Mr. Cameron Ovey of the British Museum (Natural History) in London. The connection cannot as yet be considered definite. Still, it shows what intensely interesting results can be derived from collaboration between oceanographers, climatologists and specialists on micropalaeontology.

Assuming for the present that the interrelation dem-

PLATE 6

R. Pettersson

DR. FRED PHLEGER AND HIS PLANKTON SAMPLERS

FORAMINIFERA × 20

PLATE 7

GOING ASHORE .

L. Bruneau

J. Eriksso

. . . TO A PECULIAR ISLAND (JAMESON'S STRAND)

PLATE 8

A DRAGON ON JAMES'
ISLAND

. Eriksson

THE AUTHOR WITH
A LITTLE OWL

PLATE 9

THE LARGE RING-NET

J. Eriksson

TOWING THE RING-NET ON
THE SURFACE

onstrated by the graph will be substantiated by current
investigations, one obtains a rough estimate of the total

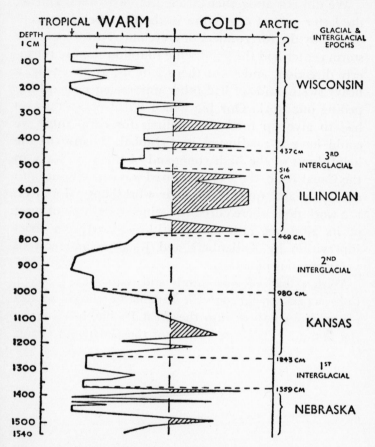

Fig. 7.—Succession of climatic periods as shown by Foraminifera.

length of time required for accumulating the 50 feet of
sediment thickness represented by the core. It is about
six hundred thousand years. This would mean a rate of
accumulation of one foot in forty thousand years, or an

increase in the thickness of the sediment carpet of one inch in one thousand years, a reasonable supposition.

We did not altogether escape the hurricanes. During the latter part of our cruise in the Caribbean we were chased by the forerunners of a cyclone. Fortunately the storm center had the good sense to follow a more northerly direction, and from there sent us, as an envoy, a heavy swell. And we had other unforeseen mishaps impeding our work. Our big winch failed us, so that we had to give up further soundings for cores until we could have it readjusted in Cristobal. Thanks to the helpfulness of the high command of the U.S. Navy in the Canal Zone, the work required was carried out both efficiently and quickly in their workshops. Moreover, the work done there cured the winch definitely of most of its ailments, although it still required very strict supervision by Kullenberg and Jonasson and cost us many anxious moments.

With a load off our minds and with great expectations, we passed through the Panama Canal and set our course from Balboa into the great Pacific, heading for the famous "Enchanted Isles" of the Galapagos group.

Chapter 7

THE ISLES OF ETERNAL SPRING

Right on the Equator, in the middle of the tropical zone, where the sun at noon pours down a vertical torrent of flaming heat, one finds the Enchanted Isles. There, by a freak of nature, a spring-like coolness prevails, as on a sunny day in May in far-off Sweden. The cause of this mild temperature is the ocean, or rather the cool water which rises to the surface to the south of the Galapagos group, raised by the mighty sweep of the Humboldt Current. This upwelling water is rich in nutrient salts which give rise to an abundance of marine life, plankton organisms, fish, sea-birds and even sea lions, lavishly nourished by the bounties of the ocean.

The giant tortoises, laying their eggs on the sandy beaches of the islands, are now almost exterminated. In bygone centuries they made the group a favorite resort of the desperadoes of the high seas, the wild buccaneers. These loyal pirates named the different islands after members or retainers of the Royal House of Stuart. From this base the terrible Morgan set out on his cruises, ravaging the prosperous city of old Panama and laying waste other harbors along the isthmus. Some cen-

turies before him an intrepid seafarer among the Incas
of Peru, called Yupangui, is believed to have reached
the islands in a primitive ship. He described "mountains in flames," probably identical with the volcanoes
of the Galapagos Islands, some of which have been active
quite recently.

We of the Swedish Deep-Sea Expedition had been
charged by our specialist on the Pacific islands flora, Professor Skottsberg of Göteborg, to send a landing party
ashore on one of the islands. He would have preferred
the largest of the whole group, Albemarle, where he
wanted us to collect indigenous plants high up on the
hills. Meanwhile the *Albatross* was to work to the south
of the islands, investigating the upwelling water, its
myriads of plankton and the deposits on the bottom.

Our first call was on the southwestern island, Chatham, where we had to report to the Ecuadorian authorities. They were represented by a pleasant and rather shy
young officer, Teniente de Fragata, who had recently
taken charge of the score of soldiers stationed there. He
readily gave us permission to spend several days on the
uninhabited James Island, but warned us not to make
any landing on Albemarle. This island was then occu-
pied by deported criminals, of which some were notorious desperadoes from the mainland. They were expected
to cut each others' throats in the course of about two or
three years; until then the island was not considered a
healthy spot for peaceful visitors. The American naturalist and author, Ainslie Conway, whom we had the
great luck to meet on Chatham, warned us in still more
emphatic terms to leave Albemarle alone. With Mrs.
Conway, he had spent several years in the Galapagos,
beginning with James Island and then settling on Flor-
eana. After World War II the Conways had returned to

James Island, until they were evacuated to Chatham by order of the Ecuadorian authorities. The official reason given was that they were in imminent danger of having their throats cut by visitors from Albemarle. Conway himself scoffed at the idea and strongly encouraged us to visit James Island, the peculiar charm of which had completely captivated him.

Besides excellent information and advice, the Conways presented us with oranges of rare fragrancy, grown on Chatham. Teniente de Fragata, who had evidently been flattered by the snapshots we had taken of him and his awe-inspiring guard, gave me a few delicious pineapples grown in the interior of the island. We also photographed him against a memorial bust of the great Charles Darwin. The Darwin Society of London had recently set it up in commemoration of the young Darwin's famous visit to the Galapagos group in the *Beagle* in 1835.

The shores and the lower levels of the islands suffer from regular droughts, and are almost desert-like. On the hill tops and the hill slopes there is more rain, which supports a not-too-abundant vegetation. Our visit happened to coincide with the height of the dry season, when the cold, upwelling water has its greatest effect. The surface temperature is then reduced to 60° F., or even less, as compared with 80° F. or more prevailing in the surface of the equatorial seas. Consequently much of the vegetation was dormant, the rest being scantily supplied with moisture from wet nocturnal fogs, known as *garua*. From a botanical point of view our visit was, therefore, not fortunately timed. But this adverse circumstance did not prevent the leader of our landing party, Dr. Eriksson, from getting a fair collection of rare Galapagos plants.

Early on a September morning, five of us were put ashore from the *Albatross* motor-launch in the James Bight on the southern side of the island. Pitch-black lava rocks alternated with beaches of snow-white sand. Numerous scarlet spots scattered over the rocks turned out to be large crabs, *Grapsus grapsus,* which, at our approach, fled with incredible swiftness into crevasses and holes in the lava. Basking in the sun were lazy though formidable-looking sea lizards; they resembled dragons pictured in fairy tales. A sea lion, startled from his siesta, slid out of a cave and regarded us with astonished eyes.

We soon found the deserted site of Conway's former house. It took considerably more time to find our way to their freshwater spring, the only water supply on the island during the rainless season. Our walk there over sand and gravel, alternating with a natural pavement of hard volcanic tuff, and with the mighty "Sugarloaf" as a background, had an indescribable charm. Scattered trees with white twigs reminded us of a Swedish orchard in early spring, when lime is used to prevent ravages by the "frost butterfly." Between the trees were green shrubs, miraculously in flower, and fine-leaved acacias in which small birds were singing jubilantly.

The fearlessness of the birds was remarkable. We had many occasions for surprises of this kind during our visit to James Island. The small finches Darwin described, with beaks of varying size and shape, with plumes of different shades from light gray to black, were among the boldest. Sometimes an inquisitive finch perched on one's shoulder and started a twittering conversation. Perfectly delightful were the small Galapagos doves with rose-colored breasts, coral-red feet and turquoise rings around their eyes. They crowded about us,

especially on our visits to the spring, which we kept
well covered, when not in use, with a sheet of corrugated
iron as a protection against wild goats and asses. As soon
as the birds saw us approach the water, they came in
flocks for a drink and a bath. We obliged them as far as
we considered compatible with the strict economy we
had to observe in using the precious water.

Our five days on James Island were the thirstiest I
have ever spent. Fetching our daily supply of water to
our distant camp from Conway's spring was quite a
strenuous undertaking.

Soon we were ready to march with our kit, including
tents, hammocks, clothes, guns, cameras, cooking-gear,
provisions and water, toward the foot of the northern
hills, where our base camp was pitched. Conway had
warned us against the intervening river of *pahoehoe*
lava, which we had to traverse, and which he described
as perfectly awful.

Our first encounter with this volcanic product was
disheartening. It resembled a choppy sea suddenly transformed into black and very brittle stone with a curiously
twisted and distorted surface. Where blocks had broken
loose, or where a crevasse had opened, the color of the
lower layers varied from soot-black through a dirty
brownish yellow to a color reminding one unpleasantly
of putrefying flesh. The worst of it was that the lava
fragments, sharp-edged like crushed glass, cut into the
soles of our sturdy boots and reduced our rate of progress to intolerable slowness. Add to this a vertical flood
of pitiless sunlight, burning neck and shoulders, which
were weighted down by our heavy marching-kit. As one
of the party remarked, the ghastly lava river gave the
impression that here the devil must have been making
taffy for his offspring and had allowed the pot to boil

over. Nearly exhausted, we finally reached the opposite shore of the lava stream. There we slung our hammocks from trees growing close to a miniature crater. Its jagged crests were crowned with giant *Opuntias,* the cacti characteristic of the Galapagos Islands. In a narrow cleft we discovered a dainty little owl. In spite of its protests, it was removed to the light of day and made to pose before the camera, after which it was set free. We considered the incident closed, but not so the owl. Later in the evening, as we were cooking our supper on an improvised grate built from lava rocks, the owl paid us a return visit. He flew away but soon returned with a second little owl, and both stayed quite close to us, obviously deeply interested in our culinary preparations.

Three of us devoted the following day to collecting plants and taking photographs. Meanwhile the two young apprentices from the *Albatross* were sent back over the lava river to fetch more water from the spring. We who took the opposite direction toward the hills were at first delighted with the agreeable flatness of the ground. Numerous wild asses and goats fled at our approach and we almost stumbled over a great sow. Surrounded by her numerous offspring, she grunted her strong disapproval at being disturbed, and, with them, promptly disappeared into the thicket. Much less shy than these wild descendants of domestic animals were two large birds of prey. They were magnificent Galapagos buzzards, one of them very dark, the other a speckled brown. They followed us from tree to tree during our wanderings and cheerfully posed before the cameras. When I took the liberty of poking one of them in the chest with a long stick, he suffered it patiently; afterward he carefully rearranged his ruffled feathers without moving from his perch.

During our climb up the steep hillside we came on the roughest ground I have ever met: a very steep slope with scattered lava blocks, treacherously giving way under our feet, slippery stems of fallen trees and prickly shrubs, which made the climb strenuous in the extreme. Finally we reached the summit and were rewarded by a magnificent view of the nearest islands. Albemarle, shifting in color from rose to black and, further to the south, Indefatigable Island, just visible as a blue shade on the glittering sea. By contrast, the landscape immediately before us was decidedly sinister. The dark lava river in all its horror cut a broad streak across the surrounding brushwood and the scanty verdure. On its other side a grayish-red crater rose abruptly skyward. Afterward we found that it contained a small lake of salt brine surrounded by brilliantly green succulent herbs. The view before us made an unforgettable picture of blue sea, black volcanic wilderness and early spring charm.

The following day my son and I volunteered as water-carriers. I was imprudent enough to go around the "Sugarloaf" on the land side, grossly underestimating the distance we had to walk. Several hours later than I expected we arrived with parched throats at Conway's spring, drank our fill and replenished our water-bottles. In our absence our comrades collected botanical specimens and tried their luck at shooting wild pigs. They bagged a sow and two suckling pigs. One of the latter was roasted on a spit over the fire, and was consumed with relish.

Our last day on James Island we devoted to our friends the sea lions. They were enjoying their siesta on shelves of lava rocks overhanging the water. Deep clefts filled with emerald-green sea-water, spanned by natural bridges of lava, ran in from the shore. The ocean swell thundered in and out through subterranean channels. By friendly prodding we convinced the sleepy sea lions that the time had come for a dip. Once they had taken the plunge, they rose to the occasion and gave us a brilliant display of swimming and diving stunts. Sea lions are born actors and are eager for applause. The majority of our landing party soon followed their example and bathed, surrounded by the sea lions, who evidently considered the whole thing a great joke.

With pangs of real regret we saw on our return hike the stately hull and the four masts of the *Albatross* rise over the horizon on her way to fetch us from our island. We had had a rather strenuous time, and had suffered from a chronic thirst, but we were loath to reembark. Unshaven and unwashed—the scarcity of water had made our ablutions perfunctory—we were brought on board. There an excellent lunch and ice-cold beer consoled us for our Paradise Lost.

Chapter 8

IN THE EASTERN PACIFIC

In his excellent book, *The Floor of the Ocean*, Reginald A. Daly, the famous geologist of Harvard University, writes: "The major mysteries of land geology itself are planetary, and to a large extent their secrets lie hidden under the ocean. The learning of those secrets will mean a wide extension of the field of knowledge and therewith a new call on human courage." Obviously these riddles can best be solved through collaboration between geology and oceanography—which was one of the main purposes of the Swedish Deep-Sea Expedition.

One of the enigmas of geological science concerns the origin and the age of the enormous depression in the Earth's crust which forms the basin of the Pacific Ocean. One suggestion is that it represents the scar left behind at the birth of our satellite, the Moon, when she was torn out of the body of the Earth by a cataclysmic tidal wave, raised by the Sun some three thousand million years ago. Most geologists, however, consider the depression to have been caused by internal forces in the Earth's crust, forces which have shaped and reshaped its features, lowering the ocean floor and raising the continents. The same forces may also have raised island "bridges," spanning the oceans from one continent to another, and later, in a following geological age, have again submerged them under the water surface.

If it were possible to prove that such land-bridges have actually existed, it would help biologists and palae-ontologists to explain how plants, wingless insects and other non-aquatic animals have been able to spread across water-filled chasms thousands of miles wide and thousands of fathoms deep.

In the central Pacific Ocean the island groups, like the submarine ridges supporting them, show a distinct trend from the west-north-west toward the east-south-east. According to some authorities, this is a sign that they are remnants of old transoceanic land-bridges, which became almost totally submerged many millions of years ago.

The new technique used on the *Albatross* for study-ing the deep ocean floor seemed to offer opportunities for attacking this fascinating problem experimentally. A gradual sinking of a land-bridge or of a festoon of islands should be evident from the character of the sedi-ment deposited after the sinking occurred. Perhaps such a change of level might be apparent in the strat-ification of a very long sediment core. And, if it were not possible to raise cores sufficiently long to display such strata, there was still the probability that the echoes from exploding depth-charges, thrown back against the bed-rock beneath the sediment carpet and recorded on our oscillograms, would reveal the shape of the basin, so as either to refute or confirm the supposed change in level.

Our course across the Pacific had been chosen with this purpose in mind. In general, practical considerations already mentioned kept us within or near the belt of equatorial calms in order to work in a minimum of ocean swell and wind. Fortunately for us, that part of the ocean offers problems of great interest, both as to the bottom and as to the water masses over it, problems well worthy of a close study by modern methods.

After leaving Balboa, the *Albatross* was at first headed toward the west-south-west. Work was carried out in the Gulf of Panama and in the open sea beyond it. The cores raised there were exceptionally rich in remains from coastal vegetation carried seaward, which had become waterlogged and had sunk to the bottom. Dr. Eriksson made a couple of successful horizontal hauls with a large ring-net (Plate 9) at depths of 400 and 800 fathoms. A catch of fantastically shaped deep-sea fish and invertebrate organisms was brought up from the realm of eternal darkness. Some of them were provided with luminous organs of amazing efficiency. The light-economy realized by these living lamps of the deep is much better than that which human ingenuity has so far achieved. This biological light is practically "cold," *i.e.* it is almost all concentrated within the visible parts of the spectrum. Hence no energy is wasted on infrared heat rays which make up by far the greater part of the output of our most efficient electric lights.

Our first objective was the Galapagos group, described earlier. There five of us spent several days ashore. After those who remained on the *Albatross* had finished the study of the water strata and the bottom sediments to the south of the group, and had taken the landing-party aboard, her course was set west-north-west, so as to give our oceanographers an opportunity for taking sections on the Equatorial Counter-Current. On the way, numerous attempts were made to raise long cores and to sound the thickness of sediment by means of exploding depth-charges. The bottom configuration in this part of the Pacific was not very favorable for such work. Its general ruggedness made the use of long coring-tubes too risky and also gave rise to a confusing multitude of echoes from the explosions, and we repeatedly hit hard bottom—a surprising phenomenon at depths of between 2000 and 3000 fathoms. In one instance, a broken-off fragment, sticking in the bit of the corer, proved that the hard bottom consisted of a lava bed due to a submarine eruption or extrusion of magma of fairly recent date. We repeatedly met discouraging bottom conditions as our cruise continued across the Pacific and Indian Oceans. (Fig. 8.)

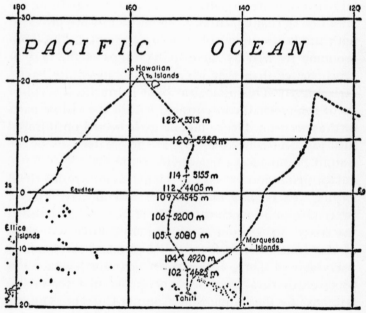

Fig. 8.—Part of the *Albatross'* course over the Pacific.

Obviously, submarine volcanism has played a dominant part in shaping the bottom configuration of the two oceans. By far the greatest number of islands there are volcanic cones, built from the ocean floor by repeated eruptions. Most of the summits protruding above the ocean surface have been broken down by wave-action and are crowned with diadems of living coral. In certain cases the eruptions have been so sustained and intense that the volcanic cones have been raised thousands of feet above the surface, giving rise to large islands, some of them, like Hawaii, with active volcanoes still on their summits.

The experience of the Swedish Deep-Sea Expedition proved that these outbreaks of the subterranean fires have acted also in a horizontal direction, producing lava beds of considerable expanse. The formation of a level bed of lava, at the point of encounter between red-hot magma from below and ice-cold water from above, was made possible by the fact that at depths greater than 1200 fathoms the water pressure exceeds the so-called "critical pressure" of water vapor. At great depths, therefore, water cannot "boil," so that the extrusion of lava proceeds without any violent disturbance at the surface. It is indeed possible, not to say probable, that a similar formation of a lava cover on the top of more ancient sediments has occurred several times in the same locality, intervening sediment layers being formed between the lava beds during prolonged stages of volcanic inactivity. In such instances, a multiple stratification of lava beds, alternating with sediment, occurs.

Possibly this may also explain the surprising results produced both in the Pacific and Indian Oceans—the failure of the exploding depth-charges to evoke any *deep* echoes. Nowhere west of the Galapagos Islands were the

echoes recorded as coming from a greater depth below
the surface of the sediment than about 1000 feet. If
present at all, they generally came from reflecting surfaces situated much nearer the bottom. Compared with
results from the open Atlantic as well as from the Caribbean Sea, where echoes from many thousands of feet
down in the sediment were recorded, this result is surprising.

It seems to contradict the widely accepted opinion
that the Pacific Ocean is the oldest sea of the world, and
ought to have the thickest sediment carpet on its rocky
floor. However, the thickness of the carpet depends not
only on the age of the ocean, *i.e.* on the total time of
accumulation, but also on the *rate* of accumulation,
which is known to vary widely. It seems prudent, therefore, not to draw far-reaching conclusions from the sediment soundings until they have been fully analyzed and
discussed.

Considerable judgment had to be exercised in the
choice of length of the coring-tube to be used. There
was always the risk of the long and rather fragile structure bending or breaking, if it happened to topple on
a steep slope when it reached bottom.

When we approached the eighteenth parallel north,
a southerly course was set, affording our oceanographers an opportunity for a second crossing of the equatorial current system.

The greatest water movements occurring on our
planet are not those of the Amazon nor of the Missis-
sippi Rivers, but those of the great ocean currents. They
carry incomparably larger water masses and, incidentally, spread warmth from the tropics to higher latitudes
less favored with solar heat; or inversely, they transport
the Arctic and Antarctic cold toward the Equator. Most

PLATE 10

J. Eriksson

R. Petterson

THE CORING-TUBE BENT AGAINST A LAVA BED

L. Bruneau

THE BUST OF CHARLES DARWIN ON CHATHAM ISLAND

PLATE II

A COCONUT GROVE

L. Bruneau

LUNCH WITH DR. LAVAUD

PLATE 12

L. Bruneau

TAIPI BAY

conspicuous among the great arteries of the ocean are the Equatorial Currents. On both sides of the Equator they carry warm surface water from east to west, which gives rise to an accumulation of water off the eastern coasts of the continents.

Especially in the Pacific Ocean this movement of water from east to west is of gigantic dimensions. It maintains a slope of the surface, which is the cause of the remarkable Counter-Current, separating the two

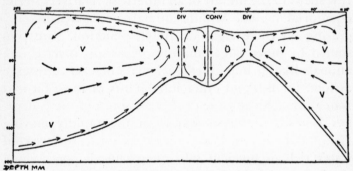

Fig. 9.—The Atlantic Convergence.

Equatorial Currents and moving in the opposite direction, *i.e.* from west to east. This east-bound current is confined to a narrow strip of water, only a few degrees of latitude in width, lying just north of the Equator. It extends from near the Philippine Islands to the vicinity of the Central American coast. The surface slope which sustains it is not impressive, having only a tenth of a million gradient.

The dynamics of the Counter-Current are most interesting. In the Atlantic Ocean they were carefully studied by the oceanographers of the German *Meteor* Expedition, 1925-27. The schematic cross-section reproduced in Fig. 9 has been taken from their reports. As is seen from the diagram, there are regions of water rising from some depth and spreading over the surface, so-called "divergences," with an intermediate zone where the water descends from the surface, a "convergence." The ascending water carries with it reserves of nutrient salts, especially phosphates, and when it meets daylight near the surface it provides food for an abundant vegetation of floating microscopic algae—the "grass" of the ocean meadows—which are thus concentrated along narrow strips in the middle of an otherwise relatively sterile equatorial region. Minute animals or "zoa-plankton," grazing on these algae or "phyto-plankton," are consumed by other larger marine organisms, invertebrate animals like shrimps, medusae, etc. These in turn serve as food for fish and other inhabitants of these favored water strata. Such is the case to the south of the Galapagos Islands, where suction from the rapidly moving Humboldt Current brings up to the sunlit surface cold water rich in nutrient salts. The same happens along the Equatorial Counter-Current.

This remarkable fertilization of the ocean surface from below also affects the bottom sediments, which consist largely of the calcareous shells and the siliceous skeletons sinking down from the upper water strata. During the epochs of extensive glaciation which occurred in our Quaternary Age, the trade winds and travelling storms in high latitudes hardly could have remained unaffected by the climatic changes. Whether the curiously stratified condition of our long cores taken near the equatorial region was due to climatic changes with the rhythm of the great ice ages will be known when the composition of these cores is analyzed.

During our crossings and recrossings over the equatorial current system, the oceanographic winch was working at short intervals night and day. Like the beads of a rosary, the "reversing" water-bottles were clamped to the thin but very strong steel wire rope with the "reversing" thermometers. The latter recorded the temperature of the surrounding water to within 0.01°C. at depths, where they were made to reverse by means of "messengers," small metal cylinders with an axial hole in the center through which ran the instrument line. Their impact on the water-bottle made it turn upside down and, at the same time, hermetically enclosed a sample of the water. Another messenger automatically released by the impact ran down to the next deeper water-bottle and made it reverse, and so on. Brought up on deck after all bottles had been reversed at their proper depths, the temperature was read on the reversing thermometers and the water in each bottle sampled for analysis by our chemist.

Between the complete oceanographic series at predetermined "stations," still more frequent observations of the temperature in the uppermost water-layers were made by means of an ingenious recording thermometer called the "bathythermograph." An interesting result from the oceanographic series deserves special mention. Beneath the relatively shallow Counter-Current, generally at depths betweens 50 and 200 fathoms, the water is almost stagnant. There the all-important oxygen has become practically exhausted, partly by bacterial processes which accompany the disintegration of plankton organisms sinking from the surface, and partly by the respiration of marine organisms. The lowest figure we found for the residual oxygen contained in this intermediate water layer, to the west-north-west of the Galapagos Islands, was only 0.04 c.c. per liter of water, or less than one per cent of the saturation value found at the surface.

In the course of other oceanographic observations, Dr. Jerlov seized an opportunity for measuring, by an ultra-sensitive optical method, the amount of fine particles suspended within different water-layers. As a rule the mid-ocean water masses are transparent, but characteristic differences in their low turbidity were found among the different strata. At certain depths a kind of "cloud" made up of a great number of particles was observed. Whether such "clouds" are mainly ultra-fine organic fragments settling from the "ocean meadows," or extremely minute ash particles from recent volcanic eruptions, or, at greater depths, particles of sediment from the deposit stirred up by bottom currents, is still an open question. Anyway, these particle studies have proved very useful for characterizing the vertical water movements in the zones of divergence and convergence.

Measurements of the submarine daylight of different colors were also a feature of our oceanographic studies. The electric winch for the light-measuring apparatus, mounted in the stern of the ship, was set in action and the electric current from the submerged "photo-elements" or rectifying cells was measured on a galvanometer of high sensitivity placed in the main laboratory. An unforeseen complication in these measurements was caused by sharks swarming around the ship. Evidently they mistook the glittering apparatus for a tidbit sent down for their special gratification and made attacks on it, sometimes biting through the electric insulation around the cable.

By way of retaliation, and in order to instill in them respect for modern science, many sharks were caught and brought on deck, where they were promptly killed by a bullet through the head. Because of the voracious appetites of these creatures, we had, to our great regret, to abstain from swimming. The danger from sharks has long been a subject for discussion. Some optimists assert that the sharks mean no real harm but simply have an innate curiosity for the taste of human flesh. But none of us had a mind to test this hypothesis.

Other more welcome visitors came to us by air. A large black albatross took a rest on our deck, where it was duly photographed before being set free. A still rarer guest was a snow-white "tropical bird" adorned with a long scarlet tail-feather. For a few minutes it perched on our bulwark before taking wing again, one of the loveliest sights of the tropical seas.

Birds were rare in the part of the ocean we were traversing. We saw no more than a few dozen during the five weeks we cruised from the Galapagos Islands to the Marquesas. By then our water supply was running short, and with considerable relief we saw, on a fine October evening, the wild rugged rocks of mighty Nuku Hiva appear through rifts in the golden clouds over the setting sun.

Chapter 9

NUKU HIVA AND TAHITI

Anyone reading Robert Louis Stevenson or Herman
Melville on the Marquesas is captivated by their descrip-
tions of the marvellous scenery, the wild volcanic rocks
and the alluring coral beaches, which impart a romantic
beauty to these wonderful islands. There is, however,
an undertone of deep sadness running through their
tales of the slowly disappearing people, who only a century ago were the most numerous and the most beautiful inhabitants of the South Seas.

The *Albatross* dropped anchor in Taiohae Bay on
the south coast of Nuku Hiva, largest and most picturesque of the Marquesas Islands. Volcanic cones rising
steeply out of an emerald-green sea protected our ship
against all except winds from the south, which hardly
ever bring gales in this part of the ocean. But for the
fantastic shape of the ridges above and the luxuriant
vegetation covering their slopes, we might have mistaken our surroundings for an inner part of a Norwegian fiord.

Dr. Lavaud, a young Frenchman who was acting as
deputy-governor of the island, paid us a call, with the

shipping agent, a jolly old Scotsman whom everybody called "Mr. Bob." They gave us a hearty welcome and at once drew up a program for our entertainment. First, Dr. Lavaud proposed a visit to Père Jean of the Roman Catholic Mission. After that we were to attend a football game between the apprentices on the *Albatross* and a local team coached by Père Jean. For the following day, Dr. Lavaud had invited the officers and staff to a *déjeuner Tahitien* in the Residence, from which the Tricolor proudly waved.

We gratefully accepted. After nearly six weeks on the high seas without a glimpse of ship or land, with only the immense blue expanse of the Pacific Ocean around us, we felt in need of entertainment. "Mr. Bob" took us to see the Reverend Father, a man in his early thirties with a long black beard and melancholy eyes which twinkled humorously whenever he spoke of his parishioners. He had introduced various games, including football, as a means of keeping the boys from idleness and, above all, alcohol. For the natives there is strict prohibition on the islands, but somehow spirits are smuggled in with disastrous effects on manners and morals. Fortunately the boys had taken well to sports. They played football with passion and considerable skill, to the dismay of our own boys, who were completely out of training. Our champions were conclusively beaten in the Nuku Hiva-Sweden match, largely owing to Père Jean's skillful playing. Dressed in his black soutane and shod in heavy boots, he had displayed an astonishing agility, although the temperature was well over 90°. It was most interesting to watch both the players and the spectators. Practically the entire small population of the valley had turned up to watch the game and there was no doubt about their enthusiasm.

On our visit to the Mission, Père Jean showed us beautiful examples of native handicraft, especially woodcarving, in which his flock excelled. To my embarrassment he presented me with a beautifully carved ceremonial oar which I had greatly admired and which he insisted that I accept. For several weeks I was at a loss how to repay him for this magnificent gift. Then I had a brainstorm:—a football! The ball used in the game was rather the worse for wear after years of hard use. At last, in Honolulu, I succeeded in finding a ball of the right size and shape, which I sent as a Christmas gift to Père Jean. May it last long and help him in keeping his dusky flock on the path of virtue.

Shortly before noon the following day we were received at the Residence by Dr. Lavaud and his charming hostess, a most attractive young lady of mixed French and Tahitian blood. She was arrayed in a splendid "parero," and very little else, with white star-like blossoms in her black tresses. By way of welcome we were all decorated with *leis* of sweet-smelling frangipani hung round our necks. The Captain and I, as guests of honor, received an extra *lei* each.

We were first taken to see the kitchen, the traditional pit dug in the ground and filled with heated stones on which the main courses, a suckling pig and wild fowl, were being roasted, spreading an appetizing odor through the entire garden.

The table set for lunch was the stone floor of a long balcony, covered for the occasion with giant banana leaves and adorned with huge bunches of scarlet hibiscus flowers. An abundance of choice tropical fruits was spread along the table, including opened coconuts with their refreshing juice available to thirsty throats. There were also bottles of excellent hock, cooled on board the *Albatross,* since neither ice nor electric current for refrigerators is available on the island. As an entree we were served delicious fish, cured raw with chives and with a sauce of coconut milk. There were giant fresh-water prawns, roasted bread-fruit, fey-bananas, and an endless variety of local delicacies. The meal was magnificent. Unused to the squatting posture on the floor, some of us felt slightly uncomfortable, but the friendly atmosphere and buoyant spirits made the repast one of the most enjoyable I have ever had.

Afterward all the guests, including several of Dr. Lavaud's native assistants and their wives, had coffee in the great hall. Nuku Hiva coffee is famous for its aroma. Ukuleles and other musical instruments were produced and dancing began Our lovely hostess acted as *prima ballerina* and her hula-hula, performed in a raffia skirt, aroused great admiration. When Marquesans hear or produce music they are transformed and their faces radiate joy.

We had another opportunity of watching this form of musical intoxication on one of the following nights, at a native dance arranged in our honor by Dr. Lavaud. It took place in a large copra shed, dimly illuminated by a single kerosene lamp. At one end of the shed was a low platform for the orchestra, consisting of young boys adorned with *leis* and with white flowers in their ebony-black hair. The leading musician, young Bernard, had been imprisoned for some minor offence, but he had been triumphantly brought out by the island's lone policeman, crowned with flowers and given a banjo, which he played like a virtuoso. Late that night, when the dance was over, Bernard was taken back to solitary confinement. I am happy to say that he spent only the nights in jail. In the daytime he was free to work in the governor's garden or to go visit his friends.

The dances we saw were extremely interesting. They are very ancient, and the accompanying words are not understood by most of the dancers. They have been passed by word of mouth from generation to generation. One picturesque dance was a pantomime, evidently commemorating a daring sea expedition of long ago. A row of women flanked by two rows of men, all in sitting posture, moved their arms and bodies as if they were rowing a canoe to the accompaniment of a rhythmical, melodious, rather melancholy song. Another dance was weird beyond the limits of propriety. In a polite translation, its English title would be "The Dance of the Love-Sick Pigs"—the native title is more outspoken and the dance is frowned upon by the missionaries. A dispensation was granted on our account and we were told that the same dance, slightly censored, had been performed before the Duke and Duchess of York (afterward King George VI and his Queen) when they visited Nuku Hiva twenty years earlier.

The dance opened with the performers seated, but as the tempo and the excitement rose, incited by a solo dancer who carried out a turbulent *pas seul,* every second man suddenly jumped on to the shoulders of the one ahead of him and with violent gestures, accompanied by realistic grunts, enacted the emotions of an amorous pig. The effect was comical and at the same time a little frightening. Had we been shipwrecked on Nuku Hiva a century ago, the same dance, performed before the feast at which we would have been served as the *plat du jour*—"long pig" is the traditional term used by old cannibals—might well have been the last earthly spectacle we would have been allowed to witness.

Afterward the real ball began and dancing became general. It was fascinating to watch the fair boys from the *Albatross* swinging the dark-haired, bare-footed girls, descendants of the old warriors who had terrified Melville and are described in his *Typee*. They seemed to get on famously, although conversation was necessarily limited to a few words of broken English. As an aftermath, crowds of boys and girls visited us on board ship during the days that followed. They always wanted to have music and to dance on deck. They listened with rapture to our phonograph—as long as rumbas or jazz were played. But when we tried classical music they suddenly lost interest and strayed away. To them music must be rhythmic and syncopated or else it becomes a tedious noise.

Science was not neglected during our stay at Nuku Hiva. Dr. Eriksson headed a botanical expedition to the high, and rarely visited, Tovii Plateau, where he made a fine collection of indigenous plants, especially mosses and lichens. The opportunity was also seized by Arrhenius for taking borings from one of the very few peat bogs known in the tropics. After it is analyzed for pollen grains, it will perhaps provide us with a key which can be used in dating the pollen grains we hope to find in the deep-sea cores taken from surrounding parts of the ocean bottom.

On another day we went on an excursion in Dr. Lavaud's motor launch to the eastern Taipi Bay, the most fertile and, in earlier days, the most populous of the Nuku Hivan valleys. At the present time the population of the entire island has dwindled to a mere 800, a small fraction of its number a century ago. Euro-

pean diseases and European vices have wiped out the
Marquesans at a terrific rate. At the end of World War
I, Spanish flu, as it was then called, wiped out whole
villages. Nevertheless, Dr. Lavaud is optimistic about
the future. The pure Marquesan race is nearly extinct,
but mixture with Tahitian and other South Sea races
produces a more resilient stock. The birth-rate is soaring and infant mortality has been reduced to a minimum. On one of the islands the population is said to
have doubled in the course of six years, an almost incredible increase. We could see for ourselves that the
huts were swarming with children and babies, and more
were evidently expected in the near future.

On the last day of our stay on Nuku Hiva we went
on an excursion into the narrow Hakui Valley, east of
Taiohae Bay, right up to its famous waterfall, a bridal
veil of silver draped over a chasm of black volcanic rock
more than 600 feet high. The landscape in that valley
is the most fantastic I have ever seen. Volcanic cones rise
nearly vertically skyward from a jungle of tropical trees
and shrubs, including wild coffee bushes. Trold Fiord
on the west coast of Norway, and Fischleintal in the eastern Dolomites, are the only parallels that come to mind.
It is beyond the capacity of the camera to capture the
beauty of this primeval wilderness and the contrasts it
offers between pitch-black jagged rocks, delicate emerald-green verdure, and white foam of cascading water.
It is a memory to cherish for a lifetime.

With deep regret we left this wonderful island of
eternal summer and our charming friends, who had
showered us with gifts and decorated us with *leis* of
haunting fragrance before they went ashore. As I
watched the Sentinel Rocks, guarding the entrance to

Taiohae Bay, sink below the horizon, the sad South Sea poem rang in my ears:

The palm thrives, the coral grows, but man dies.

The Isle of Bliss, the Queen of the South Seas, and the New Cytherea—these are different names given to Tahiti, which in earlier times was also called Otaheiti. The beauty of the landscape and of its inhabitants was praised by early visitors, whereas the morals, especially of the women, were described as regrettably low. Captain James Cook, perhaps the greatest of all explorers, observed the Transit of Venus on June 3, 1769, from a promontory on Tahiti, along with Green and the Swedish naturalist Solander. Cook cannot be accused of prudery. Nevertheless, Cook and later visitors were scandalized by the levity of the Tahitian womenfolk and by the dishonesty of the men. The missionaries who followed in their wake in the nineteenth century had a tough job when they tried to instill piety into the pagan souls of the Tahitians and to induce them to conceal their shapely bodies in ugly European clothes.

On board the *Albatross,* approaching the capital town of the island, Papeete, situated on its northern coast, we were full of expectancy. The first impressions were not overwhelming. We came straight from Nuku Hiva, where we had met with the loveliness of wild rocks and luxuriant vegetation. Papeete to us seemed rather tame and a little dull, like a Swedish bathing resort, although not as clean. Its mixed population is dominated by Chinese and Chinese crossbreeds. The infiltration by industrious and penurious Chinese is a serious problem throughout the Pacific island world. What remains of the aboriginal race, largely mixed with foreign blood, is exploited by the yellow traders.

The weather, which at first was rainy, soon brightened. We northerners couldn't help succumbing to the wonderful beauty of the island, to its strange and delicately tinted flowers, and to the charming hospitality of its people.

The *Albatross,* wherever she put in, was greatly admired. In Papeete, where no European expedition had made a landing since the visit of the *Dana,* we received crowds of visitors from ashore. Our reception was most cordial. There are few Swedes or other Scandinavians in Tahiti, but those who were there gave us a hearty welcome. Other residents—French, English, American and the Tahitians themselves—entertained us wholeheartedly during the ten days we spent in Papeete. Two of the youngest members of the staff mysteriously disappeared from the ship. We found out later they had been the guests of a local chieftain near the southernmost point of the island. For a whole week they shared with him and his family their sorrows and joys, joined in the fishing expeditions, and at night danced the hulahula in the Tahitian moonlight.

The rest of us led a more sedate existence in Papeete and its surroundings, although there was no lack of amusement. We were taken on a visit to a military outpost located at an altitude of 2500 feet, from which we had a gorgeous view of the harbor of Papeete and the sea beyond. We climbed higher up, following a rocky path, until we reached the dizzy Col du Diable, nearly 4000 feet above sea-level, and were rewarded by an awe-inspiring view of wild and precipitous canyons where masses of clouds came pouring down the slopes, inundating the festoons of graceful palms. Afterward we were served an excellent lunch on an overhanging terrace from which the coral reefs of the Tuamoto Islands—the

"Dangerous Archipelago"—were visible 70 miles away, white patches in the sapphire sea. Our kind host, a great lover of music, gave us as an accompaniment to our lunch a recording of Beethoven's Ninth Symphony, exquisitely played by the Vienna Philharmonic Orchestra. I have never listened to the immortal slow movement in a more marvellous setting.

My son and I went on a two-day visit to the wonderful island of Moorea. The volcanic rocks there are piled high, forming structures surpassing those of Nuku Hiva and Hawaii. Again, the quiet bay with its glassy surface reminds one of the Trold Fiord in Norway, but a Trold Fiord with steep slopes draped in tropical verdure, and the shore fringed by a border of strange flowers exhaling a fragrance which still haunts us. Our kind American hosts, Mr. and Mrs. Kellum, received us like old friends and tried to make us stay for a couple of days longer. They promised us exciting wild boar shooting; these animals sometimes reach a weight of two hundred pounds or more and are quite dangerous. The Kellums have been living in this earthly paradise for nearly twenty years, save for a break during the War when they had worked on the mainland. Their little kingdom stretches from the coral beach up to a jagged ridge at 4000 feet above sea-level. We were initiated into the art of catching fish by means of a throw-net and spearing large freshwater prawns.

Our indefatigable Dr. Eriksson made an excursion to the crater lake, Vahiria, high up in the mountains of Tahiti. His object was to catch an eel which, according to native legend, has external ears; but he did not succeed. Instead he brought back a rich collection of rare plants and splendid photographs.

When the inevitable hour for our departure came, the

crowd which collected on the quay to see the *Albatross* off included the elite of the island beauties with whom our staff and the young apprentices had become friends. There was a wonderful collection of *leis* on the main deck of the *Albatross* which, according to an old custom, were thrown into the sea when we left the harbor, in token of our intention to come back to this bewitching island.

However, the hard realities of life on Tahiti should not be passed over. It is a very expensive place. The rate of exchange on the franc of *L'Océanie* is more than twice that of the Parisian franc. Flourishing export business to the United States and profits from the tourist traffic are the main reasons for this anomaly. On the other hand, taxes are very low, but import duties keep prices at a ruinous level. When we left Tahiti, therefore, our hearts were full and our pockets empty.

PLATE 13

OFF TAIHOE BAY

PLATE 14

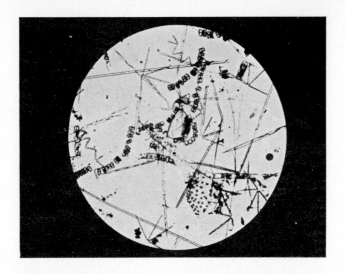

MICROSCOPIC 'GRASS' DIATOMS FROM THE MEADOWS OF THE SEA
(× 100)

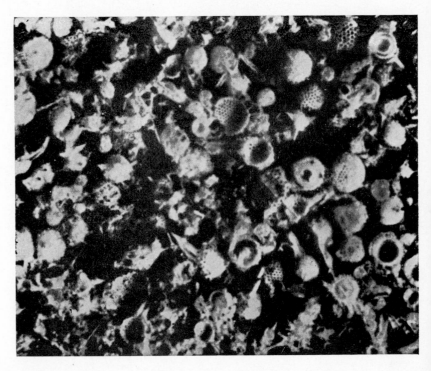

RADIOLARIA (× 100)

PLATE 15

LIGHT MEASUREMENTS IN
THE TRANSPARENT SARGASSO
SEA

J. Eriksson

THE GEOTHERMOMETER
IS PUT IN PLACE

PLATE 16

OUR DOCTOR WEARING A HAWAIIAN 'LEI'

J. Eriksson

FISHING ON HAWAII

Chapter 10

FROM TAHITI TO HAWAII

On August 19, 1875, H.M.S. *Challenger* left Hilo, the main harbor on the island of Hawaii. In Volume 4 of the famous "Reports of the Expedition," Sir John Murray and his co-author Renard state: "An excellent meridian section was made between the Sandwich and the Society groups." Within the short space of about one month, observations were made at seventeen different stations at depths varying from 1500 to 3000 fathoms. The sediment samples collected were among the most interesting taken during the whole cruise. They comprised samples of red clay, radiolarian ooze, globigerina ooze and volcanic mud. Several of the cores, short though they were, displayed a distinct stratification. By means of the dredge and the trawl, strange marine organisms, many of them new to science, had been brought up. In addition, a wealth of so-called manganese nodules, which are curious growths formed at great depths, were raised from the ocean floor, with ear-bones of whales and teeth of giant sharks of the Tertiary Age. The last-named relics, found in the uppermost layer of

97

the sediment, are striking evidence of the incredibly slow rate of decomposition.

Thanks to the courtesy of the officials of the British Museum (Natural History) I had, many years earlier, received a jar containing sediment from the *Challenger* station 276 (lat. 13°28′S., long. 149°30′W.). It consisted of red clay showing two different shades of color and, in addition, a number of small manganese nodules. Measurements made of the radium content showed very high values, about twenty times higher than those typical of continental sedimentary rocks. The external and therefore most recent parts of the manganese concretions were also rich in radium. The layers showed a rapid decline in radium content inward, which can be explained by a gradual disintegration of the element to 50 per cent of its original value in about 1600 years. From these data, I computed the rate at which the nodule had grown to be about one millimeter, or 0.04 inch, in one thousand years.

Now we were able to visit some of these *Challenger* stations and to repeat the sampling with the aid of more powerful modern technique. I had long cherished this hope, which was at last realized. Our work between Tahiti and Hawaii, following closely the course of the *Challenger* though in the opposite direction, was begun at the *Challenger* station 276 already mentioned. Warned by earlier experience of the roughness of the Pacific Ocean floor, Dr. Kullenberg thought it prudent to limit the length of the coring-tube to 35 feet, which was nevertheless about twelve times as long as the corers used on board the *Challenger*. This precaution was amply justified by events; for only about half the length of the coring-tube could penetrate into the deposit. It met with a hard layer, as was proved by deep indentations in the steel bit of the corer. Although in this case no sample from the hard layer was obtained, there is little doubt that it consisted of lava from a submarine eruption which occurred several million years ago.

Eagerly this sample from the records of the deep was examined. Its uppermost layers were of a fairly homogeneous clay, chocolate-brown in color and rich in tiny siliceous skeletons from radiolarians (Plate 14). Near its lower end the core displayed a complicated and highly interesting stratification with alternating layers of varying color and structure, with differences also in its micro-fossil and its mineral particles. Prominent among the latter were twin crystals of phillipsite, a curious product of complex and little-known chemical reactions at great depths. Obviously the processes forming the crystals must have taken place after the volcanic eruption which spread a lava bed, impervious to the coring-tube, over deeper layers of more ancient sediments. The actual chronology of events at this most interesting station must be left to future analysis.

Near other *Challenger* stations which we visited as we continued on our course, where echo-grams indicated more suitable bottom conditions, considerably longer cores were obtained, a few of them between 40 and 50 feet in length. The remarkable transition from red clay or radiolarian ooze to an almost white globigerina ooze, discovered by the *Challenger* expedition near the Equator, was also manifest in the *Albatross* cores. This sediment, with its high content of calcareous shells from tiny surface organisms, was found there at great depths where ordinarily one would have expected red clay with little lime. This startling find Murray and Renard attributed to the abundance of plankton organisms in the sea surface above, an explanation which is supported by our own observations. The reason for this abundance is the peculiar water circulation, revealed by the oceanographic sections. Within and near the Equatorial Counter-Current there are zonal strips of ascending deep water, rich in nutrient salts, which fertilized *from below* the "meadows of the sea," sustaining a rich vegetation of microscopic algae. In their turn these serve as a food reserve for plankton animals and hosts of larger organisms grazing below the surface.

An interesting observation which we repeatedly made when crossing one of these strips of fertilized water was the suggestion on the echo-grams of a "false bottom"— an accumulation of organisms reflecting the ultrasonic waves. This mysterious layer, which has also been recorded by other observers, moves vertically up and down from a depth of some hundreds of feet in daytime to near the surface at night. Similar movements of the hosts of shrimp which serve as food for the herring shoals off the coast of Scandinavia are well known in our northern waters. Our attempts to catch samples from this cloud of living matter failed, probably because the animals were too swift to be captured by our slow plankton nets. In certain cases the "false bottom" disintegrated into distinct short streaks on the echo-gram, similar to those produced by a shoal of fish.

The sea bottom along our course had in general the same rugged character which we had come to know— and to fear—during our cruise through the eastern Pacific. The echo-grams showed two or more intersecting curves, and neither the corers nor the depth-charges could be used with the desired results. Twice a sudden change from a smooth to a rugged bottom led to loss of gear. In one case our large dredge, towed over the bottom at a depth of 2700 fathoms in order to collect manganese concretions and sharks' teeth, was fouled by a hummock and was lost. Another accident happened to the coring-tube, when the lower 30 feet of a 50-foot coring-tube was broken off and lost along with its precious contents. On a third occasion, the corer came up unbroken but with a sharp bend due to an encounter with a hard bottom, presumably a lava bed covered by a thin veneer of deposit. Apart from the loss of precious gear, such accidents involved an equally serious loss of time. One had to take such vicissitudes with philosophical composure—but it wasn't easy.

Measurements of sediment thickness by means of exploding depth-charges produced results similar to those farther east. Echoes from surfaces showing the thickness of the sediment were repeatedly obtained, even where the coring-tube met with a superficial lava bed. But these echoes hardly ever came from a greater depth below the sediment surface than between 150 and 900 feet, even when the quantity of explosive was doubled or tripled in the hope of detecting deeper and fainter echoes. This lack of deep reflecting surfaces in the deposits of the Pacific Ocean, an experience which was later repeated in the Indian Ocean, forms a striking contrast to the conditions in the open Atlantic and in the Caribbean Sea.

There are three possible explanations for this surprising result. One is that sedimentation in the Pacific and Indian Oceans has proceeded at a much slower rate than in the Atlantic. Another is the occurrence of lava beds which prevent detection of deeper echoes; such layers, interspaced in the deposits at different depths below its surface, form more or less effective barriers to the sound waves. The third possibility, namely, that the age of the

Pacific is much less than that of the Atlantic, runs contrary to views generally held by geologists.

On our journey between Tahiti and Hawaii we made the first attempt on record to measure the downward increase of temperature in the deep-sea bottom. A geothermometer of special construction, consisting of a steel tube 35 feet long and containing in its lowest, pressure-resistant part a protected, highly sensitive spirit thermometer, was driven down into the deposit. By means of a clockwork mechanism which opened and closed a stopcock after given periods of time, the difference of temperature between the surrounding deposit eleven meters down and the very constant temperature of the water immediately above the bottom could be registered to within 0.01°C. The downward "geothermal gradient" thus obtained was unexpectedly high. There was a temperature difference of about 0.5°C. at a "depth" in the sediment of nearly eleven meters. Even allowing for the fact that heat conductivity of the sediment, due to its high water content, is lower than that of most continental rocks, this measurement leads to a rate of geothermal flow nearly as high as or even higher than that generally met on land.

Unfortunately, attempts to repeat measurements of this kind during the following months generally failed because of imperfect thermal adjustments of the clockwork, which made it stop at the ice-cold temperatures prevailing at great depths. A second successful measurement at about the same depth in the western Pacific ended with the same result, which strongly supports the conclusion already mentioned.

Similar measurements made afterward by other expeditions in the Pacific Ocean, although by means of different instruments, seem to confirm the pioneer work of the *Albatross* in this new field, which, according to Professor Harold Jeffreys, of Cambridge, an authority on the subject, is of prime importance in contemporary geophysical research.

Chapter 11

HAWAII

Some twenty to forty million years ago, there was a terrible turmoil in the central part of the Pacific Ocean. Through enormous fissures in the ocean floor, white-hot lava welled up out of reservoirs hidden deep in the Earth's crust. In many cases the only lasting effects from such submarine eruptions are extensive lava beds, superimposed on layers of more ancient sediments. But along two great circles on our planet, running from the west-north-west to the east-south-east, the fires raged incessantly, piling up gigantic volcanoes which lifted their flaming craters thousands of feet above the water surface.

The result of this titanic struggle between the molten lava and the ice-cold bottom water is visible in the shape of volcanic islands. They form the nucleus of the island world in the equatorial part of the vast Pacific Ocean. Their outpost to the east is the Galapagos group. Farther west comes the Marquesas Islands and lovely Tahiti, with the numerous "dangerous islands" of the Tuamoto archipelago between them. These latter are also of volcanic origin, although their visible parts are diadems of snow-white coral set on the submerged brows of volcanic cones which rise steeply from the ocean floor. Farther north, on the other side of the Equator, lie the glorious Hawaiian Islands.

Captain James Cook—perhaps greatest of all explorers of the eighteenth century—on his search for the fabled Northwest Passage, was the first European to sight these crown jewels of the Pacific, on January 18, 1778. In honor of his patron, the Earl of Sandwich—at that time First Sea Lord of the British Admiralty—he called the group the Sandwich Islands. Cook continued his voyage toward the uncharted north, but failed to find the Northwest Passage, a feat accomplished nearly a century and a half later by the Norwegian explorer Amundsen. Instead he followed the coast of Alaska, adding greatly to the geographical knowledge of his day. On his return voyage, Cook met his death at the hands of Hawaiian warriors in Kealakekua Bay on February 14, 1779.

The later history of the kingdom of Hawaii under its seven kings is a fascinating tale of energy and cunning, of bloody slaughter and wise statesmanship. During the last decade of the eighteenth century the eight largest islands became united under the great King Kamehameha I, of Napoleonic stature, about the same time as his counterpart in France began his meteoric rise to the imperial crown. To the end of his days, Kamehameha, unlike Napoleon, remained the unchallenged lord of his island kingdom, which his son and descendants governed after him until 1872, when the male line of the dynasty became extinct.

The seventh and last king of Hawaii was the highly gifted David Kalakaua. By a treaty with the United States he paved the way to a brilliant economic future for his realm. Also, inevitably, he increased American political influence. Perhaps still more fraught with serious consequences was the increased cultivation of sugar cane, which called for importation of laborers from Asia. This influx, which King David himself started, ultimately led to his own race being hopelessly outnumbered by Japanese, Chinese and Filipino immigrants and their descendants.

Kalakaua and the greatest of all romancers of the Pacific islands, Robert Louis Stevenson, became great friends. During half a year's stay near Honolulu, R.L.S. frequently visited the king. He expressed great admiration for His Majesty's ability to consume five bottles of champagne in rapid succession without any apparent ill effects. "In fact, His Majesty only got more dignified with each new bottle!"

King Kalakaua did not belong to the Kamehameha dynasty. He was a descendant of Kamehameha's most trusted councillor and had been elected by the Hawaiian legislature. He died in 1891 during a visit to San Francisco. He was succeeded on the throne by his sister Queen Liliuokalani, renowned for her musical gifts. She composed the beautiful national anthem "Aloha Oe." After a reign of only four years she was forced to abdicate. A democratic movement aiming at a union with the United States then got the upper hand. Since that time, the Hawaiian Islands have remained a territory with its own legislature under the sovereignty of the U.S.A. At present there is a strong movement in favor of its being admitted as the forty-ninth state of the Union, which would, *inter alia,* carry with it the doubtful blessing of being allowed to partake in the election of the president.

On a day late in November of 1947 the *Albatross* was drawing near the capital of the Hawaiian Islands, Honolulu, situated on Oahu. We had been eagerly awaited.

There were frequent inquiries by wireless regarding the day and hour of our arrival, about the number of the staff and the crew, invitations to me to give a talk before the Chamber of Commerce, etc. Drawing near Oahu we met one airplane after another, swishing down toward us like seagulls trying to ward off an intruder. Then other planes drew near with cameras photographing us from the air. Finally motor-boats, also with cameras trained on our ship, came out in swarms.

Our reception in the harbor of Honolulu was overwhelming. With a glorious sunset as background, during which we observed the "green ray" for the fourth time during our cruise, we slowly entered the spacious harbor set in a panorama of volcanic ridges. The *Albatross* offered a vision of dreamlike beauty as she slowly approached the quay. A thirty-piece orchestra, supplemented by a quartet, was waiting for us. One melodious song after another was sung in our honor. One of the women danced a graceful *pas seul,* to the delight of our young apprentices.

Then the reception committee came on board to shake hands—mostly Scandinavians shouting Scandinavian words of greeting. They were representatives of the Scandinavian association "SweNorDen," which had chosen the reception committee, while the mayor of Honolulu had given orders for the musical entertainment.

Men of Swedish, Norwegian and Danish descent play a considerable role in the Hawaiian Islands. Names like Olsson, Knudsen, Mattson, Larsen, Svensson and others command respect all over the islands. A full program had been planned for our entertainment. Excursions, picnics, visits to museums, receptions, coffee parties—the Scandinavians are great lovers of the delicious Hawaiian coffee—and other fetes filled up such of our time in Honolulu as was not devoted to private sightseeing. Our young apprentices, who were very popular wherever we landed, were made members of the distinguished "Canoe Outrigger Club." It fronted on Waikiki Beach where one could indulge in the favorite Hawaiian sport of surf-riding. A huge Kanaka took me in hand. He roared his approval when I—alas, not too often—managed to rise on my surf board at the right moment and was carried toward the shore by an emerald-green, foam-crested Pacific roller.

I cannot possibly recount all the kind hospitality we were offered, not only by the Scandinavians but also by others—both "Caucasians" and descendants of the old Hawaiian aristocracy. The islands are a melting-pot of many races. There are, among others, 175,000 Japanese and almost as many Chinese, Filipinos and other Orientals. Racial interbreeding goes on apace, and one meets with many splendid types of its results in the streets of Honolulu.

With very few exceptions, the Japanese have proved loyal to the country of their adoption. Many tens of thousands of young Japanese soldiers fought bravely under the Stars and Stripes in North Africa and in Italy during World War II.

One gets the impression that here, right in the center of the Pacific Ocean, a new type of humanity is being developed, in which the energy of the "Caucasians," the wise self-control of the Orientals, the diligence of the Chinese, the high spirits of the Kanakas and the helpfulness of the Filipinos, are happily blended. The city of Honolulu itself is largely a product of American western expansion, with resplendent multicolored neon signs at night, long rows of automobiles, and rather ramshackle houses which seem to have been put together in a hurry. On higher ground, against the surrounding hills, the style of architecture becomes more distinguished. There one finds the University of Hawaii, the Bernice P. Bishop Museum, and the old palaces of the royal house and the nobility, now largely converted into government departments or into hotels for the elite.

At a round-table conference arranged by the University of Hawaii, representatives of various natural sciences had an opportunity of seeking information from all the specialists on the staff of the *Albatross,* each of whom gave a brief summary of his own share in the work on board. Frequent were the visits made on board the ship; on the last days of our sojourn, there was an almost incessant stream of visitors who came to see us and our equipment.

We, in turn, saw the Bernice P. Bishop Museum, founded by an American who had married a wealthy Hawaiian princess and who had built and equipped it as a memorial to her. We saw exquisite collections of native art and handicraft. Priceless mantles made of red and yellow feathers were the most treasured regalia of the old Hawaiian kings. Now many of the treasures are stored in the Bishop Museum. A single one of them was said to contain feathers of 80,000 birds. The director of the Museum, Sir Peter Buck—whose mother was a Maori and whose father was an Irishman—took us around the ethnological department, and his colleagues showed us the other collections.

Our stay in Honolulu was longer than we had intended, for we had to repair damage to our equipment. With a couple of the staff, I seized the opportunity of making a visit by airplane to the greater island, Hawaii, situated about 120 nautical miles from Oahu. It was a great experience to see from the air these wonderful islands, thrown up from the deep by volcanic forces and sculptured by erosion into fantastic shapes of many colors, from straw-color to red, in a setting of deep blue water.

Arriving at the main port, Hilo, we were driven around the island by car, which also took us up to the Halemaunau crater. It had been in full blast only a few years earlier. During our visit the volcano was in repose, but large blocks of lava thrown for great distances gave an idea of the violence of the eruption. We asked our guide when the next great outbreak might be expected and he answered: "In one hundred and thirty-two years." This happens to be the length of the last pause in the activity of Halemaunau. But our informant added that strict punctuality of outbreaks cannot be expected from volcanoes or from women.

During our drive we repeatedly crossed broad streams of black lava which had run down the slopes of giant Mauna Loa in its earlier eruptions. Local tourist societies have provided signboards indicating their dates. This dating of lava streams reminded us of the vintages we had come to know on Madeira: 1792, 1808, 1826, etc., and these reminders evoked an intense thirst, lava being extremely dry.

On returning to Oahu, we found its familiar outline very tame compared with the magnificent sweep of the contours of Hawaii with its giant volcanoes. On Oahu the volcanic fires have been extinguished for countless ages.

Our stay in Honolulu coincided with the sixth anniversary of the attack on Pearl Harbor, which was commemorated both in the churches and at the graves of thousands of victims. "*That* will never happen again," we were assured when we called on the high command of the Pacific Fleet, who had given us the greatest assistance from the naval workshops, etc.

However, although Japan is now out of the picture, there is another great power reported to have more than eighty large U-boats cruising in various parts of the Pacific Ocean. World politics may well become more and more concentrated on this gigantic ocean, now that Europe is almost bled white and does not seem able to take its old part in the struggle between East and West. Uncle Sam is preparing for this eventuality on Hawaii, his foremost outpost to the east.

Chapter 12

A VISIT TO KING DAVID

Scattered over the wide expanse of the Pacific Ocean, supported by low reefs of dazzling white coral, one finds decorative green bouquets of graceful palms. They are generally arrayed in festoons, and surrounded by a protecting reef which converts the ocean swell into foaming breakers. Their eternal song fills the ears with unforgettable music.

These charming rings of verdure set in the deep blue of the ocean are called atolls. Their origin has been the subject of prolonged discussions among scientists. Modern geology usually ascribes a volcanic origin to the base of the atolls—a cone formed by a submarine eruption rising steeply toward the surface. The original crater has been broken down by wave action, and become crowned with a tiara of coral which defies the gales and affords protection for the children of sun and sea, the dusky inhabitants of the South Seas.

In one of his masterly books, *In the South Seas,* Robert Louis Stevenson has drawn an immortal picture of his friend King Tembinok of Apemama, an autocrat of a highly original type. He was surrounded by a bodyguard of twenty wives who rowed his great canoe and worked in his "palace." Their recompense was plugs of tobacco, which they generally lost back to their lord in a game of cards of his own invention.

The size and draught of the *Albatross* made her entry through the narrow channel into an atoll dangerous. However, our oceanographers wished to measure the ultraviolet component of submarine daylight within the transparent waters of a lagoon, where their instruments were not exposed to the ocean swell. For this purpose we intended to visit the island of Ponapé in the Carolines, but because of the unavoidable delay in Honolulu we had to abandon this plan. In consequence, we had to celebrate Christmas and New Year on the high seas. We dined together on deck on Christmas Eve, and celebrated the day in true Swedish style with the special dishes of far-off Scandinavia, and with Christmas trees, Christmas songs and Christmas cheer.

Early in January 1948 our course lay close to the Kapingamarangi atoll, in the Gilbert Archipelago. Our friends at the Bernice P. Bishop Museum of Honolulu, who knew the atoll from their ethnological studies, strongly advised us to touch at this rarely visited island, which is under the benevolent rule of a native king called David, and of his wife Queen Viora. We carried a letter of introduction, written in the Kapingamarangian language, and various gifts to Their Majesties and their subjects.

With much anticipation we started from the *Albatross*, which had been laid-to at a safe distance from the reefs. Our motor launch, commanded by Captain Krafft himself, soon carried us through the "Greenwich Passage," the only entrance to the lagoon. Our approach had evidently been noticed—ships are rare visitors to the atoll—and a number of smart and surprisingly swift outrigger canoes bore down on us. One of these we took in tow, and its captain, climbing over into our launch, piloted us to the main island where King David resides. His chaplain, an elderly gentleman who combined piety with a keen eye for business, knew a few words of English. Across half a mile of brilliantly clear water we reached the main pier, where a crowd of brown, benevolently grinning commoners met us and conducted us to the royal palace, a wooden bungalow of one room surrounded on three sides by a veranda.

King David, a rather stout, elderly gentleman attired for the occasion in shorts and a jacket, received us in a most friendly manner, as did his queen. Queen Viora resembled a farmer's wife from southern Sweden, except for her dark complexion. In contrast with his namesake in the Bible, King David is monogamous, and he is extremely virtuous. Two wooden chairs were reserved for Captain Krafft and me, each covered with a white bath towel. His Majesty, his cabinet and his chaplain were seated on wooden benches. In spite of my hasty studies of the Kapingamarangian language, my share in the conversation was rather perfunctory. However, I made a heroic attempt to read aloud the letter of introduction from the Bernice P. Bishop Museum, and was assured by grunts of approval from His Majesty that he had understood some of it.

After having drunk His Majesty's health in coconut juice—officially prohibition is the rule in his kingdom and the import of spirits and wine is strictly forbidden —we had a look at the curly heads of his faithful subjects who were crowded at the open windows. Bars of chocolate and candy to the younger among them, and bars of soap and illustrated American papers to the women, created goodwill and we were invited to watch and to take photographs of their various occupations, cooking, rocking cradles, weaving, net-making and canoe-building.

Their dwellings are primitive enough. Four stout poles support the roof made of leaves, with mats woven from the same material serving as walls. The passages between the huts are narrow and covered with coral sand of dazzling whiteness. All over the village were canoe sails spread to dry. The greeting "Maria koe," learned from Dr. Emory's dictionary, always evoked a friendly response. The shapely bodies and smiling faces of the inhabitants had a comeliness, not to say beauty, of a type we northerners could not help admiring. Another amiable feature was the generosity with which gifts were showered upon us—belts of raffia, necklaces of shells and even small models of canoes were ours without asking. We could only return their kindness with American cigarettes, which were highly appreciated, although officially tobacco is also frowned on in Kapinga-marangi. The same word stands for "Christian" and "non-smoker"—a fact I communicated by letter to a friend of mine, a bishop in Sweden, who is an inveterate smoker. Nevertheless Camel cigarettes are a kind of currency in the islands. Even King David absentmindedly accepted the packet of the forbidden ware which I slipped into his pocket.

Like other inhabitants of the Pacific islands, the subjects of King David are well content with the food they get from the sea and from their vegetable gardens, added to their staple food and drink derived from coconuts. Enjoying abundant food obtained with a minimum of effort, they cannot see any reason why they should toil for more. In King David's happy realm, taxes are almost non-existent. Nor has it occurred to King David's paternal government to extort death duties or inheritance taxes from his subjects when they leave their earthly paradise.

When Jerlov and Koczy had finished their light measurements in the lagoon and the rest of us had satisfied our curiosity about South Sea life and customs, I asked for a second audience with His Majesty, which was readily granted. I tried my best to express my gratitude to him and his government in a string of vowels, of which the Kapingamarangian language is mainly composed, and at the same time expressed my hopes of soon seeing him and Queen Viora in Göteborg. With the inevitable coconut juice, we drank to improved relations, commercial and political, between Kapingamarangi and Sweden. We bowed to each other, we smiled, and finally we thumped each other's back in an affectionate embrace—the only time, so far, I have had that privilege accorded me by a reigning monarch—and we parted great friends. As a final gift, His Majesty conferred on me a beautiful raffia girdle decorated with rare shells. The respect this royal gift evoked from his suite convinced me that the decoration must be equivalent to the Garter or the *Croix de la Legion d'honneur*. Its additional advantage is that it can be worn with shorts.

The royal chaplain agreed to sell me an outrigger canoe, a dug-out 20 feet long, which was carried back to Sweden on board the *Albatross* and is at present arousing the envy of other sailors on the Gullmar Fiord. Somewhat later, I discovered that His Reverence had been too smart for me; he had given me his oldest and most dilapidated dug-out, and moreover extorted an extra five dollars above the price agreed on. I record a solemn warning to my readers not to buy canoes from royal chaplains without careful inspection.

Through the tortuous channel, our motor boat soon carried us out to the *Albatross*. From King David's island we headed westward for the great deep off the Philippine island of Mindanao.

Chapter 13

THE MINDANAO DEEP

From the fog-bound Aleutian Islands in the far north to the sunny Fiji and Tonga groups in the South Seas, a series of island arcs spans the Pacific Ocean. They mark a region of permanent unrest in the crust of the Earth, with frequent earthquakes relieving a tension built up during millions of years. To some extent this tension may be a remnant of the catastrophe in which the Pacific was formed. Whether its basin is really a "birth scar," due to the violent separation of the Earth and the Moon, is still debatable.

A very curious feature is that these island festoons are flanked to the east by deep furrows in the ocean bed, the famous troughs or trenches, in which the greatest depths are found. This abrupt change in level from island mountain chains to ocean depths has its counterpart along the opposite side of the ocean, where the snow-clad ridges of the Andes rise as high above the sea surface as the deep troughs descend below it.

The tension inherent in this transition zone between ocean depths and continental heights not only causes the earth tremors already mentioned but also gives rise to gigantic seismic waves, spreading across the ocean at velocities of a thousand feet or more per second. On April 1, 1946, such a seismic wave, due to a submarine landslide near the Aleutians, wrought havoc along the north coast of the Hawaiian Islands. More than a hundred school children, who had been paddling near Hilo and had imprudently followed the retreating water seaward, were drowned by the cataclysmic wave on its return.

Within the solid crust itself, another kind of even swifter seismic wave travels from the source of disturbance, and near its epicenter the sea may work even greater havoc than the fury of the seismic wave.

A close study of these elastic earth vibrations has enabled seismologists to draw important conclusions regarding earth structure, both in the crust and in the deep interior. Thanks to their interpretaion of transoceanic tremors recorded by seismographs, we know that the rock-bed beneath the sea bottom in the eastern and the central parts of the Pacific Ocean has a composition different from that of the continents. A deeper, basaltic layer of the crust there rises up to the surface of the ocean floor. Most of the oceanic islands are built up of the same material. The granite layer, which forms the uppermost shell over the continents, is missing until one reaches the so-called "andesite line" in the western Pacific, where a layer rich in silicates is superimposed on the heavier basalt. In 1928 one of the greatest ocean depths was discovered to the west of the Philippine island of Mindanao by the German research ship *Emden*. It took the sound waves emitted from the ship more than 14 seconds to reach the receiving hydrophone after they had been reflected against the sea bottom. This time interval, the echo-time, corresponds to a depth of water of about 10,500 meters, or about 6000 fathoms.

Our unforeseen delay in Honolulu obliged us to omit one planned stop in the Carolines and a visit afterward to the greatest Mindanao Deep. From Kapingamarangi, therefore, we followed a course westward toward the southern end of the Mindanao trench, with a maximum depth exceeding 5000 fathoms.

Thanks to this change in our plans, we avoided two typhoons which ravaged the northern Carolines, but they sent us reminders in the shape of contrary winds and an adverse swell, which considerably reduced our speed. While under way, several long cores were raised from depths between 2000 and 2500 fathoms. As was to be expected at this moderate depth, they were much richer in lime than those raised in the central Pacific, *i.e.*, in the region of red clay and of radiolarian ooze.

After sailing for several days over moderate depths, we saw the echo-graph draw a falling curve which finally reached the 4000 fathom mark. After setting our course to the north, an increase in depth by several hundred fathoms was registered. Near the fifth parallel north, our deepest echo-sounding for the whole voyage gave 9400 meters or about 5100 fathoms. Had we pursued our course to the north, in another couple of days we should have reached the Emden Deep. Being already behind our scheduled time, and lacking a cable sufficiently long for coring operations at such enormous depths, we wisely desisted. Our deepest core was taken from 4300 fathoms where, to our surprise, the corer was stopped by coarse sand after penetrating only eight feet below the sediment surface. Considering the great depth and the distance from land where we worked, this occurrence of deep-sea sand was most unexpected. A second attempt was made to raise a core from a still greater depth by means of an extra steel cable of smaller diameter, attached to the lower end of our main cable. Luck was this time against us. When we hoisted the corer, the extension cable snapped, so that no sample was obtained from this great depth and the precious coring-tube was lost.

As a substitute we used our largest water-bottle for taking samples from the great depths for analyses for uranium and radium. The sediment soundings by means of depth-charges were disappointing. Such a multitude of spurious echoes was reflected from the slopes of the submarine trench over which we worked that no conclusions could be reached about the thickness of the sediment layer. Better results probably would have been obtained from depth-charges exploding *beneath* the sediment surface, so as to avoid the spurious echoes or reduce their intensity—a hint for future deep-sea expeditions working in this most fascinating region.

After more than five weeks on the high seas, shortage of fresh water made us change our course to the south, again cross the Line and head for the Isles of Spices, the Moluccan group. Our goal was the small volcanic island of Ternate, where we were to enjoy a few days of rest. We reached its harbor, which had been visited by the *Challenger,* and also by the *Snellius* Expedition, on January 25, 1948, almost exactly five months after our entry into the Pacific Ocean.

A Sultan of a very ancient dynasty rules Ternate and a couple of adjacent islands, with a Dutch resident-councillor at his side. This official and his staff bade us welcome in a truly hospitable manner. In his home we enjoyed for the first time the famous *rijsstafel.* Our host expressed his great regret that the number of courses had been reduced to half the orthodox figure—before World War II there used to be seventy!—an instance of the same deplorable frugality which force of circumstances has imposed on our famous Swedish *smörgåsbord*. Still, we had no reason to complain, at least not those of us who prudently avoided the most spicy items served and kept to the tamer varieties with their excellent base of boiled rice.

I had the honor of sitting beside the Sultana, a very charming lady arrayed in a sarong of exquisite *batik*. Fortunately her English was excellent, and her sense of humor also. The Sultan, her husband, who according to reports is also a very pleasant person, happened to be in bed with a touch of malaria. Moreover, he had to house a synod of Mohammedan priests. The following day, when we were invited by Her Highness to view their hereditary treasures, we heard the priests' pious prattling in the garden surrounding the palace.

An enormous, bronze-bound teak chest, such a treasure as R.L.S. would have loved to see, was thrown open to our amazed eyes. There were heavy helmets made of solid gold or silver, Spanish work from the seventeenth century, priceless Damascus swords with handles inlaid with gold, and large plates and bowls of silver, several of them of great age and weight. In glaring contrast with the exquisite workmanship of these ancient treasures were hideously ugly articles received during the last century as gifts from European kings. I was especially interested in an old fruit-salver made from the cloven shell of a *coco-de-mer* set in Spanish silver. Later during our cruise we were to visit the island in the Indian Ocean where these giant nuts, largest of all fruits, are grown.

Curio hunters on the staff of the *Albatross* found

Ternate a mine of interest. Among the treasures which were furtively offered for sale were a few skins of birds of paradise. In the Moluccan Islands these feathered fairies have been practically exterminated, but on the great neighboring island of New Guinea they abound and display a variety of multicolored plumage. Trade in their skins is strictly prohibited by the Dutch authorities. This fact, added to the high prices demanded, helped us resist the temptation, virtuously.

Our visit to Ternate was not to pass without incidents. Our indefatigable doctor had set his mind on climbing the steep cone of the volcano, notwithstanding its height, of about 5000 feet, and the tropical temperature. He was warned by the natives: the volcano is sacred, and an ascent would provoke the anger of the gods. Dr. Eriksson, whose piety never deters him from making interesting excursions, persisted, tempted by the opportunity offered for taking photographs on almost untrodden ground. Not without difficulty, a few carriers were persuaded to accompany him and Wenzel.

They started one evening after sunset so as to get over the most strenuous part of the climb during the coolness of the night. Having reached the summit the following morning, the two Swedes, to the terror of their superstitious carriers, made a descent into the crater proper. Apparently nobody before them had dared to provoke the gods in such an outrageous manner. The gods reacted promptly. The two infidels had hardly got out of the crater and started the descent before a violent earthquake shook the whole island of Ternate and made our *Albatross* leap at her moorings. The carriers instantly dropped their burdens and bolted, shrieking with terror. They swore never again to follow crazy Europeans up their sacred mountain.

Chapter 14

TO THE ISLE OF STRIFE AND
THE ISLE OF BEAUTY

Having left the open ocean behind us and escaped unscathed from the playground of the typhoons, we had no apprehensions of storms and swell during our voyage through the Sunda Archipelago. The immediate purpose of our visit to Surabaya was to replenish our shrinking store of diesel oil, which could not be expected to last us for many weeks. Our Dutch hosts in Ternate had given us a shock by telling us that it was almost impossible to obtain even moderate quantities of liquid fuel in this traditional realm of abundant oil wells. This scarcity of oil was an aftermath of the war. During the Japanese occupation, American bombers had systematically made havoc of all the oil wells on Borneo and on Sumatra. The Americans are excellent marksmen—and we had to suffer for it.

Were the Lord to gather up the sea, as Kipling says, a most extraordinary lunar landscape would stand revealed over the bottom of the Sunda Archipelago. There deep basins surrounded by islands and narrow submarine ridges abound and the bottom is carpeted with myriads of dead plankton organisms alternating with ashes and dust from innumerable island volcanoes. From an oceanographical point of view its water masses present a fascinating field of work. However, considering the very painstaking work done in Insulinde (the Malay Archipelago) by the Dutch *Snellius* Expedition in the early 'thirties, and our very limited time schedule, we refrained from any protracted work on our way from Ternate to Java. Moreover, adverse currents of considerable strength made our progress uncomfortably slow and, since we could not work our corers well by night, we had to pass by several places of interest. Such cores as were taken were eventually handed over to eminent Dutch geologists to supplement their own finds on the *Snellius*.

The crown jewel in the glittering diadem of the Indonesian islands under Dutch rule was Java. Hardly any other realm within the tropics had been brought to such a state of abundant production. Not without reason has Java had the reputation of being a model of European colonization. Nevertheless, the worm of discontent had been gnawing at its roots. Natives of Java who had acquired in Europe a superficial varnish mistaken for Western culture aroused sentiments for democratic rule, although the populace was totally lacking in the spirit of personal sacrifice and service which is the *sine qua non* of a working democracy. Discontent was fomented, Communism was rampant and the spirit of revolt spread under apparent peacefulness until the Japanese occupation and the slogan "Asia for the Asiatics" provided fuel for a devastating internal war.

After the War the Japanese invaders were rapidly expelled. At the time of our visit, the last remnants of their armies were still carrying on a guerilla warfare against Dutch troops high up in the mountains. But in place of Japan, another power had entered the arena. In 1946, during a visit to Holland, I was told that some of the cleverest of the political and economic experts of Hitler's Germany had been released from concentration camps and were smuggled over to Java by Russian U-boats. They were now assisting the leaders of the revolutionaries in their attempts to liberate Java from Dutch order and Dutch culture. The prospect of striking a mortal blow against the Dutch colonies was irresistible to Soviet rulers who have appropriated the slogan of the old Roman imperialists, "Divide and conquer."

Our expedition was now approaching Surabaya, the second largest city of Java. In order to reach the capital, Batavia, we would have been obliged to make a detour of several hundred nautical miles, largely across shallow waters which were relatively uninteresting from our point of view. On our way to Surabaya we passed close to several of the fairy islands of the Sunda Sea. Flores, Sumbawa, Lombok, and finally the beautiful island of Bali, in turn raised their volcanic cones skyward over the calm Indonesian sea.

Insulinde is one of the permanent zones of unrest in the Earth's crust where subterranean fires are most active, and violent eruptions from one or more of the hundred volcanoes are relatively frequent. The rains of ash from past outbreaks were noted by the Dutch *Snellius* Expedition in their sediment cores taken nearly twenty years earlier. Our hopes of supplementing their observations with cores from great depths and of still greater length were, for reasons already mentioned, only partly realized. Nevertheless, some quite interesting cores were raised, some of them showing a pronounced stratification and a few with a distinct greenish tinge due to organic matter, and exuding a smell of sulphur-ated hydrogen. The lower parts of a core 20 feet long raised from a depth of 60 fathoms over the Java shelf showed signs of having been deposited at a time when the depth of water was considerably less than at present. This was the case during the last glacial period; the level of the oceans was considerably reduced, for millions of cubic miles of water, evaporated from the oceans, were tied up in the vastly extended polar ice-caps. The shelf-bottom was laid bare, and broad river valleys eroded across it have been discovered by soundings. An extensive coring operation in this region would undoubtedly yield interesting results. But this was outside the main program of our expedition, which concentrated on the deep ocean floor.

We were received as old friends in Surabaya. A telegram from the commander of the Dutch Navy in Batavia bade us welcome to the Marine Station of Surabaya and promised us every assistance we might require. An excellent berth within the precincts of the naval station was accorded the *Albatross,* and a Dutch liaison officer came on board as soon as we arrived. We were promptly invited to an aperitif followed by a spendid *rijsstafel* in the officers' mess which is quite close to the quay. Later in the afternoon our kind guardian took us to his home, where we admired beautiful textiles and wood-carvings from Bali. The evening was agreeably concluded in a Chinese restaurant, where strange culinary delicacies of the Far East were served.

The following day we were taken by bus to a recreation camp for officers and soldiers, who can there enjoy their week-ends in a refreshingly cool climate some 3000 feet above sea-level. The drive took us through a fertile land planted with rice and with volcanic peaks as a background, the highest of which were shrouded in clouds. Near the road the houses had been badly damaged, first during the Japanese invasion and later during the guerilla warfare. Now and then our bus stopped in order to give our photographers a chance of taking pictures of native life on the road and in the rice-fields, with decorative mountains up to 10,000 feet high as a setting. Higher up the grade became steeper. Our bus groaned, the air was wonderfully cool, and the vegetation changed to a more temperate type.

Finally we arrived at the camp and got a magnificent view, out over the lowlands we had left behind us, toward the glittering sea, whereas to the other side still steeper slopes rose toward the mountain peaks. After a refreshing swim in the camp pool, we were offered refreshments. The hardiest among us tried the ill-famed durian; its smell reminded us of the terrible fermented herrings from the north of Sweden—one has to keep well to the windward of the plate while eating them. The taste of the durian is a surprise—a weird combination of very old cheese and strawberries with a touch of vanilla. We were taken for a walk into a narrow mountain gorge where cascading water-falls sprayed over the dense jungle growth. A flock of chattering monkeys crossed the footpath, which we followed until we regained the camp for an excellent lunch and a second invigorating dip in the swimming-pool. Returning in the bus to Surabaya, we passed through heavy downpours, giving us a foretaste of what real tropical rainfall is like.

The *Albatross* received many distinguished visitors during our ten days' stay in Surabaya, including the navy hydrographer and the director of mapping from Batavia, who had flown the 400 miles to Surabaya to inspect the Swedish expedition ship. We enjoyed much

PLATE 17

LANDING ON AN
ATOLL

Eriksson

KING DAVID AND
QUEEN VIORA

R. Pettersson

PLATE 18

R. Pettersson

MADAME POLLOCK, OUR HOSTESS ON BALI

PLATE 19

L. Bruneau

SOME BEAUTIES AND DEMONS OF BALI

PLATE 20

THE GALE . . .

J. Eriksso

. . . AND ITS
RESULT !

hospitality both from the Chief of the naval establishment in Surabaya, Captain van Warning, and from the Swedish Vice-Consul, Mr. Wieslander, and their charming wives.

Java has suffered much during World War II and its aftermath. Billions of guilders have been lost through aerial bombing and pillage. So it is not without reason that the Dutch are much annoyed with the United Nations for interfering as mediators in a crisis which the Dutch forces might have settled in a few weeks. Since our visit to Java, matters have not improved, and the prospect of a long period of peace and prosperity is slender.

The great difficulty here as elsewhere in the Far East is the absolute lack of civic spirit shown by the semi-Europeanized politicians and propagandists. Solidarity with their next of kin is considered a much more sacred duty than service to the community. When an ambitious native politician gets a leading post in a government department, his first step is to procure salaried sinecures for members of his family or clan without any regard to their qualifications. The resulting lack of experience among the new bureaucracy makes it necessary to employ a more numerous and more costly staff of civil servants than under the European regime. One may well wonder how these Indonesians with their veneer of Western culture will be able to shoulder the white man's burdens and still more, whether the patient workers in the fields and the factories will enjoy a more tolerable existence than before the War under their European oppressors.

When too much praise has been lavished on a landscape or a work of art, one develops a kind of allergic opposite reaction to it, probably due to an instinctive fear of being disillusioned. So much has been written and spoken in praise of Bali, the small easterly neighbor of Java, that I had almost developed an inhibition about its charm. Moreover, we had been warned in Ternate that Bali was ruined by the War, and that its inhabitants had become confirmed enemies of all Europeans. One ran risks, so we were told, of being fired at when approaching its coasts and of having one's throat cut if a landing was attempted.

Our Dutch friends in Surabaya scoffed at these rumors. "Of course you *must* see Bali. The island is practically untouched by the War and by the Japanese occupation. Do visit Bali! You will not regret it!"

We had been working very hard during our cruise through the western Pacific Ocean and had spent almost six weeks on the high seas without any break. And another long hop across the Indian Ocean was ahead of us. Surabaya with our hospitable and friendly Dutch hosts was too hot for recuperation. After one week there we became hungry for the open sea. Nevertheless, we succumbed to the temptation of touching at Bali, since our course took us along its southern coast anyhow. This gave us a chance of forming an opinion of our own on the reports we had received. Our friends in Java were perfectly right. We had ample reason for not repenting our decision to visit the Isle of Beauty.

It was an overcast day in the middle of February when the *Albatross* dropped anchor at a respectful distance from the shallow coast of southern Bali. A dozen of us were taken by our motor boat to the small harbor south of Denpassar, the largest town on the island and also its center of administration. A smart young naval officer, warned of our arrival by radio, was waiting for us on the pier with cars and took us to Denpassar. At a break-neck speed we were carried past quaint-looking houses within enclosures. Their narrow entrances were guarded by grotesquely shaped gods or demons carved in stone. The architecture is fantastic and quite different from that of Java. The rice-fields along the road display a whole gamut of delicate colors, from the exquisite green of the young blades to the rich golden bronze of the ripening crop. In this fertile country a new crop is planted before the harvest of its predecessor begins.

The men and women we met on the roads carried themselves both more gracefully and more proudly than the Javanese. The unclothed breasts of the women and the burdens they carried on their heads gave a dignified grace to their movements.

Denpassar, with its scattered villas and houses set in luxurious vegetation, reminded us somewhat of a Dan-ish village, magically transferred to the tropics. We were lodged in the splendid Bali Hotel, known and renowned all over Indonesia. The strong currents and the treach-erous sandbanks which lay between ourselves and the *Albatross* made it advisable to stay ashore overnight. We were extremely well housed, and the food as well as the service was beyond praise. We were introduced to the Dutch administrator, who is an ethnographer of high standing and who at once started a discussion on the difficulties of cultural exchanges and especially on the insurmountable barriers between the ideologies of East and West. He had a great veneration for our Swed-ish ethnographers, especially for our great authority on South America, the late Baron Erland Nordenskiöld.

We were conducted to sumptuous bedrooms where we slept inside tents of mosquito nets. A swift and silent "boy" looked to our comfort. But crickets, frogs, dogs, and, in the early morning hours, village cocks, made sleep difficult with their terrible din.

Next morning after an early breakfast with fragrant Java coffee, our landing-party was taken to the home of the most interesting European resident on Bali, the great Belgian painter Adrian Jean le Mayeur de Merpres. He lives quite close to the seashore about four miles out of Denpassar. His home is always open to his numerous friends. His charming wife, Madame Pollock, is an artist in her own right, the most famous among the renowned dancers of Bali. She received us in her country's traditional costume, which enhanced the beauty of her magnificent body. During our visit we were taken through the artist's perfectly lovely home. The walls are decorated with masterpieces painted by our host, saturated with tropical sunshine and representing lovely women surrounded by all the splendor of tropical flowers. The background to these pictures of haunting beauty is formed by old Balinese sculptures and gold brocade. We were invited to stay for lunch. The other members of the expedition, who had planned a motor trip into the hills, declined; but I could not resist the temptation of spending a few hours more with our host and his charming wife. It was a great pleasure to listen to his account of his life.

He started his career as an artist by painting the picturesque old Flemish towns and castles partly destroyed in World War I, in which he saw active service as an artillery officer. After the war, wanderlust drove him out into the world—to Italy, Spain, North Africa (we compared notes on the Ouargla Oasis in the Sahara which we both had visited), to the Near East, to India, and to the South Sea Islands. "My whole life," he said, "I have been in quest of the sun. Here I found it." He settled

down on Bali sixteen years ago, captivated by its haunting beauty, by its old culture, by its lovable and inher-
ently artistic people. Soon he found an ideal model in
the beautiful dancer Pollock. He made her share his
own artistic ambitions and after a few years he married
her, a step he has never had reason to repent.

Besides her own musical language, Madame Pollock
speaks Dutch and French. She is usually silent, but as
soon as art, her husband's or her own, comes up for discussion, her lovely face lights up and she joins in the
conversation. Nearly all the canvasses which adorn their
house have her as their central figure, arrayed in exquisite garments, surrounded by the splendor of her
flowers, and usually with one or two of her women
friends, as supple and as graceful as herself. With evident pleasure she posed for the camera bent over a pond
with water-lilies, picking the lilac flowers of the Bou-
gainvillea in the graceful attitude of a Balinese dancer,
or seated at the ancient Balinese handloom, with which
she produces masterpieces of textile art. Her two help-
mates, girls aged fourteen and eighteen, are perfect
beauties. One of them served our lunch.

Before that repast I enjoyed a swim on the beach with
another guest, a young air force officer. Spellbound by
the translucid water, I rashly swam toward the white
breakers off shore. "Not so far!" our host cried after me.
"There are sharks about, with a good appetite for bath-
ers." He takes his swims astride a faithful pony which
carries him out into the water. Then came a few buckets
of cool spring water to refresh us after the warm, salt
sea water. With a whetted appetite we gathered for
lunch. The food was delicious, and as a climax we were
served thick Arabian coffee with a glass of spiced palm-
wine as liqueur.

Le Mayeur recounted his experience with the invading Japanese, who landed on the beach in front of his house. Warned in the nick of time, he and his wife managed to escape in their car, taking with them their greatest treasures, his own pictures. After a few weeks he returned to look at his house, and to his agreeable surprise, found it quite untouched. The local commander of the Japanese troops asked for an interview and said: "Why did you flee before us? You are an artist and we do not make war on artists. Just carry on your work here in your home as before. No one will touch you!" This promise was faithfully kept. The only drawback was frequent visits by Japanese officers and soldiers who asked permission to see his paintings. This they did with obvious reverence and without touching any of the other art treasures scattered through the house. The considerate treatment, which contrasts strongly with the terrible tales of the invasion we had heard on Java, Le Mayeur puts down to the inherent respect the Japanese have for art and artists. For the same reason they treated the inhabitants of Bali without severity and left their buildings and their strange idols untouched.

One of Le Mayeur's chief troubles at present is his pictures, which are in perpetual demand for international exhibitions, to which they can be sent only with great precautions. Although he does not like to part with them, there seemed to be some prospects of one of his most resplendent paintings becoming Swedish property.

Le Mayeur is that extremely rare creature, a perfectly happy human being. He has had the great good fortune to be able to create for himself that very *milieu* which all his life he had been striving to realize. He is now well on in the sixties, but still enjoying perfect health.

May he long continue to enjoy the sea, the sunshine, his lovely home, and the company of his beloved model, his wife! He suggested that we should remain another couple of days in Bali, in which case he promised to arrange a performance of old Balinese dances in our honor, but I thought it my duty to decline. The *Albatross* was waiting for us, and the Indian Ocean was getting impatient. But still we had had a glimpse of Bali, the last refuge of beauty in a ruined world. We shall never forget it.

Chapter 15

ACROSS THE INDIAN OCEAN

Opinions among geologists regarding the early history of the Indian Ocean are almost as divided as their views on the Atlantic. But on one point there is agreement. Its age is assumed to be much less than that of the Pacific. Less than one hundred million years ago, the present deep basin of the Indian Ocean did not exist. At a wave of the magic wand of reconstructive geology, continents and intercontinental land-bridges have been conjured up from the deep. This resurrection of features of the Earth's crust long since vanished has been most extensive in the case of the Indian Ocean. Here, according to many geologists, an enormous continent—the mysterious Gondwana Land—once linked East Africa with Arabia, India and Australia.

There is a striking similarity between the early fauna and flora of these separate land masses, as revealed by long series of fossil remains found in their soil. After a sudden break, development proceeded along divergent lines of evolution. Such goes one of the main arguments for the existence and subsidence of Gondwana Land. In the northwestern Indian Ocean there are remarkable submarine ridges running in a north-south direction, some crowned by islands like the Laccadives, the Chagos and the Seychelles. These ridges have been regarded as the remnants of the lost continent still rising above the present level of the sea. Our longest cores do not penetrate sufficiently far back in time to span the enormous gulf of fifty to seventy million years, which are assumed to have elapsed since Gondwana Land disappeared beneath the waves. Still, a close study of their strata might possibly reveal signs of a continued subsidence of the sea bed during the last few million years.

After our unforgettable stay on Bali, the *Albatross* started on her cruise through the Indian Ocean. A strong wind from the west, gradually increasing to half a gale, forced us to steer south instead of west. The change in our course did not, as we had hoped, bring us out of the storm zone; on the contrary, we found the wind still blowing from the west, increasing almost to hurricane strength. The view from the navigation bridge over the huge waves, more than 25 feet in height, was magnificent. Although the ship behaved splendidly, the masts of the *Albatross* made angles of up to 35° from the vertical, which called for an almost acrobatic agility at meal-times.

Radio reports from Australia warned us that the storm center was following a course converging with our own. This made us turn 180°, and steer north until we had almost regained the latitude of Bali. Evidently we would have done well to prolong our visit to the Isle of Beauty and to enjoy the old Balinese dances, instead of wasting five precious days being buffeted about without any chance of doing work.

Having finally got out of the grip of this "willy-willy," as these travelling storms are called in Australia, we set our course toward the deep Sunda Trough which runs parallel to the south coast of Java. The Indian Ocean had now put on its most alluring face, and for weeks the *Albatross* moved over a dreamlike blue sea glittering in the sunshine by day and in the moonlight by night, and broken only by schools of flying fish darting up before our bows. (Fig. 10.)

The echo-graph worked beautifully during these

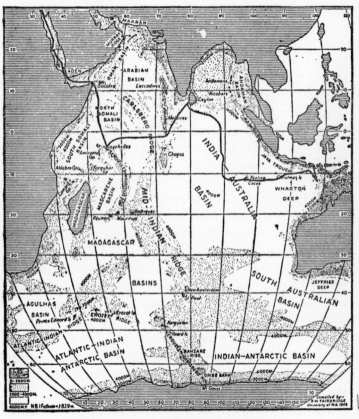

Fig. 10.—The Indian Ocean basin.

peaceful weeks, and drew a most interesting profile of the ocean floor, which almost incessantly rose and fell 1500 to 3500 fathoms below our keel. Occasionally a bank or ridge, unmarked on the charts, rose abruptly from the bottom, sometimes approaching within 500 to 600 fathoms of the surface. The maximum depth registered on our two crossings over the Sunda Trough was much less than that marked on Schott's chart—it did not quite reach 7000 meters, *i.e.* 3800 fathoms, at a position quite close to that where he recorded 4200 fathoms. Near this spot our deepest core from the Indian Ocean was raised, its length, because of the very compact nature of the sediment, being only 25 feet instead of the 33 feet expected. It had a greenish-gray color, and contained a considerable quantity of globigerina ooze, a rather surprising find at such a great depth.

After leaving the Sunda Trough, the *Albatross* followed a course close to the 11th parallel south until we reached longitude 89°E., when the course was set due north in order to reach Colombo. The abrupt changes in depth shown along our course did not encourage us to use very long core-samplers, or to waste many depth-charges on a bottom where the irregular echoes from hills and hummocks obscured the deeper echoes thrown back within the carpet of sediment. Nevertheless, a number of cores were raised, some of which showed a highly interesting stratification. One of these, nearly 40 feet long, came up from a depth of 5200 meters and displayed numerous changes in color, from gray or greenish-gray to brown or light brown, with intercalated layers of globigerina ooze. Such distinctly stratified sediments were repeatedly met near the Equator. Evidently the conditions of sedimentation there have varied considerably during the span of time corresponding to the length of the cores, say between half a million and a couple of million years. Whether the explanation has to be looked for in the varying intensity and distribution of the surface currents, or in changes in the total depth, investigations now under way may decide.

On the journey toward Colombo, a striking feature of the echo-gram north of the Equator was a perfectly level and smooth bottom, extending for hundreds of miles. Joy at this splendid opportunity for taking sediment cores of great length turned to dismay when the core-sampler came up broken in two. It had hit a hard bottom covered with only a thin layer of sediment. This hard, level surface is probably a lava bed of recent formation, something akin to the much older plateau basalts of Deccan, but differing from them in its perfectly level surface and extending over the sea bed at a depth of 2300 fathoms. Attempts to get conclusive proofs of this view in the shape of lava fragments broken loose from the hard surface, such as those found in the Pacific Ocean, were unsuccessful.

We spent ten days in Colombo, which afforded us opportunities for excursions to the Isle of Jewels, some of us visiting the famous ruined cities in the jungle, while others tried their luck at big game shooting. Then the *Albatross* again headed toward the southwest. Crossing the Equator for the thirteenth time, we were able to make an oceanographic section revealing the same characteristic stratification of the water layers which we had met on earlier crossings. Thanks to Jerlov's measurements of the varying quantity of fine particles suspended in the water, a clear picture was obtained of the water movements. There were bands of water rising to the surface from below, or descending from it, *i.e.* zones of "divergence" and "convergence." Numerous measurements of sediment thickness were made by recording the reflected waves from exploding depth-charges. Here, as in the Pacific Ocean, they gave surprisingly moderate values for the thickness of the sediment carpet, varying from 200 to 800 feet—a small fraction of the maximum values found in the Caribbean and in the open Atlantic Ocean.

An English admiral who had taken a helpful interest in our cruise had strongly advised us to visit the "paradise of the Indian Ocean," the Seychelles. Fortunately we were able to act on his advice, since Port Victoria, situated on Maki, the largest island of the group, happened to be the most convenient port of call between Colombo and Suez. We were received by the Governor, Dr. Selwyn Clarke, of Hong Kong fame, who, with members of his staff, did all in his power for our comfort and entertainment. I also had the good fortune to be driven around the island of Mahé by the Director of Education, Dr. W. E. Giles.

Mahé deserves to be called a paradise, with its towering and quaintly sculptured granitic hills clad with palms and other tropical trees and bushes, its dazzling white beaches of coral sand with quaint sea shells. Added to this, a special attraction is the absence not only of snakes but also of mosquitoes.

Our energetic ship's surgeon, Dr. Eriksson, made a botanical excursion over the hills of Mahé and collected a rich harvest of indigenous plants, especially ferns and mosses largely unknown to Swedish botanists. He also headed an expedition to the neighboring island of Praslin, which he described as even more lovely than Mahé. It is famous as the home of the *coco-de-mer,* the giant double nut of the palm *Lodoicia Seychellerum*. A couple of centuries ago its enormous fruits, which complete with husks may weigh up to 80 pounds, were known only from a few floating specimens stranded on islands and coasts of the Indian Ocean by surface currents. These nuts were considered the peculiar treasure of kings, for they were as rare and as coveted as the sperm whale's ambergris and the spiral tooth of the narwhal, believed to be the source of the fabulous unicorn-horn legend.

During our visit to Ternate, the Sultana had showed us—as I have related—among the family heirlooms a fruit-salver made of a *coco-de-mer* shell polished to the luster of ebony and set in silver. The double coconut in bygone days was held to be an infallible protection against poisoning, the professional ailment of Oriental rulers. Although its origin has been discovered, there is still a certain reliance placed in this special property, because of religious superstition. Mohammedan pilgrims to Mecca from the East Indies and China are forbidden to carry other water flasks than those made by Allah himself. His *chef-d'oeuvre* with regard to capacity is the large shell of the *coco-de-mer*. Dr. Eriksson, having won the heart of the owner of the greatest plantation of the stately palms on Praslin, brought back a rich crop of the double coconut. We enjoyed the quaint taste of their rare kernels. Like the white of boiled plover's eggs, the content is a translucent jelly, strikingly different from the liquid "milk" of the ordinary coconuts.

Leaving Port Victoria on April 15th, we started north for the Somali Deep, where we expected to find red clay. In fact, the cores raised there from depths approaching 3000 fathoms had a typical brownish tinge in the upper layers, whereas farther down there was an astonishing display of different colors, varying from nearly white through gray to black, with an occasional strong admixture of green. During the whole cruise we never saw a more pronounced stratification.

In the regions around both Ceylon and the Seychelles there seem to exist possibilities for fisheries on a large scale. Fish and fish products to the value of 25 million rupees are imported annually into Ceylon. They could certainly be got from the sea around its coasts. The great submarine bank supporting the Seychelles can probably yield still greater quantities of sea-food. Clear indications of large shoals of fish as well as of potential fish food, invertebrate marine organisms of smaller dimensions, were found on our echo-grams to the north of the Seychelles at depths of about 100 fathoms. To our great satisfaction we heard that an experienced biologist was at the time of our visit engaged in a thorough investigation of the waters around the Seychelles. This is undoubtedly the best way of founding new and developing old sea fisheries, as the splendid work carried out from Lowestoft and other centers of marine research in northwest Europe has proved.

After completing our cruise across the Indian Ocean, we reached the Bab el Mandeb Straits on April 27th and entered the Red Sea, heading north for the Mediterranean. Here our luck with the weather failed us. Very soon we met adverse wind and swell, a stiff northwesterly which at this time of the year is not infrequent and may go on blowing for weeks. Tacking against this wind proved to be very slow and working against it with the relatively weak diesel engine of the *Albatross* did not give us a speed of more than two or three knots. Not a very cheerful prospect, especially to me who, for urgent reasons, had to pay a flying visit to London and Göteborg and had made a plane reservation to leave Cairo for London on May 9th. Fearing to miss the plane, I made the Captain put me ashore in Port Sudan, intending to proceed from there by air to Cairo, an African interlude in my cruise.

No sooner had I left the ship than—as if I were a second Jonah—the wind abated and the expedition, under the temporary leadership of Dr. Kullenberg, could get along at an increased speed; they reached Suez on the very day that I arrived in Cairo, where some of the staff met me.

The highly irregular bottom profile of the Red Sea, especially in its northern part, made coring operations there very difficult. The cores, when such were obtained, consisted largely of sand blown into the sea from the adjacent deserts, and limestone fragments broken loose from the bottom.

An encouraging message, received by radio from one of our Swedish supporters just before I left the ship, exhorted us to look out for the remains of Pharaoh's host on the sea bottom near Suez. The following telegram was sent back: "Remains of Pharaoh's host discovered but are claimed by the Museum in Cairo as Egyptian Government property. Moses has mysteriously disappeared. He is believed to have reached Palestine where he is stirring up new mischief." Fortunately for me, this telegram never got into the newspapers.

PLATE 21

H. Pettersson

COCO-DE-MER

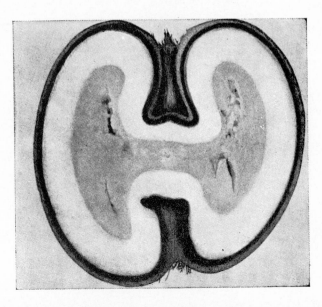

COCO-DE-MER, VERTICAL SECTION

PLATE 22

SEDIMENT WITH ASH ZONES

DEEP-SEA FISH WITH LONG 'FEELERS'

PLATE 23

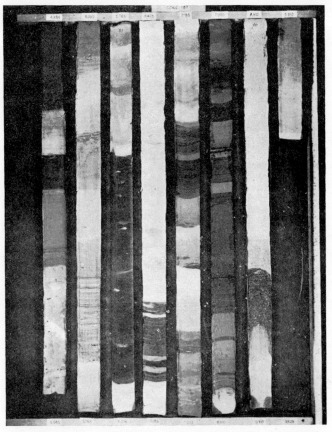

VOLCANIC ASH LAYERS IN CORE TAKEN FROM CRETE

PLATE 24

PORTUGUESE MAN-OF-WAR

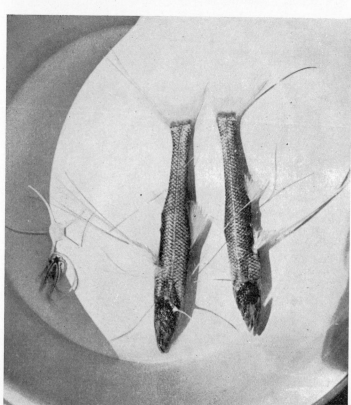

J. Eriksson

DEEP-SEA FISH WITH LONG 'FEELERS'

Chapter 16

BULLETS FROM THE COSMOS

Far out on the sturdy bowsprit of the *Albatross* I had found an excellent place for rest and meditation when the day's work was done. After dusk I used to recline there on my back, looking up toward the heavenly hosts glittering above. Below me, in the waters of the Indian Ocean, chuckling softly as our good ship split them asunder, was another multitude of stars. Unlike the stars of heaven, those of the ocean are not fixed in space, nor do they shine for billions of years. Their energy is not drawn from the inexhaustible reserves of atomic nuclei. They are instead tiny *living* lights, which flashed for a few seconds only, as the bow of the *Albatross* stirred the element they inhabit.

Now and then a streak of silver was suddenly drawn across the sky, a shooting star. An incredibly swift bullet from the Cosmos had penetrated into the top layers of our atmosphere, 50 to 100 miles overhead. Its enormously concentrated kinetic energy, suddenly transformed into heat through friction, had raised its temperature to incandescence. The extremely tenuous atmosphere high up in the region of the Northern

Lights serves as an effective shield against these glowing projectiles from interplanetary space. But for this providential aerial armor, death by meteoric stroke would be a common verdict of the coroner's jury.

Nevertheless, a few of the cosmic bullets of unusually large size are able to penetrate the whole thickness of our atmosphere and reach the surface of the Earth or of her oceans. Their massive nature has enabled them to survive the fiery flight. Sometimes they are violently disrupted with a loud report or a rolling sound as of thunder, before they come to rest on the Earth. Such meteorites and their fragments are of great interest to science, as they represent the only samples of extra-terrestrial matter available to us. Many of them are metallic, consisting of a nickel-iron alloy. By analyzing them for radium and its disintegration product helium, Professor F. A. Paneth of Durham has been able to measure their age, which may run into thousands of millions of years.

When Sir John Murray of *Challenger* fame examined samples of sediment taken from great ocean depths, he made a surprising discovery. By means of an electromagnet, he extracted from the deposit a small number of tiny pellets, one-hundredth of an inch or less in diameter. Under the microscope the surface of these cosmic spherules showed unmistakable signs of having been heated to the melting-point. Murray inferred that they were small droplets of molten nickel-iron, a spray torn off from an incandescent meteor through aerial friction, instantly solidified and slowly drawn down to the Earth.

Such cosmic spherules are extremely rare. Perhaps only one or two happen to fall on a square yard of surface in the course of a century. To hunt for these spherules on land could be as futile as the proverbial search for a needle in a haystack. At great ocean depths, on the other hand, the accretion of other material occurs with incredible slowness, increasing the thickness of the sediment carpet by a few hundredths of an inch in a thousand years. The chance of finding there the tiny cosmic bullets is accordingly increased. By means of the magnet, Sir John Murray and his co-worker Renard were able to extract as many as a score of cosmic spherules from a quart of abyssal red clay or of radiolarian ooze.

Many years ago it occurred to me that the number of cosmic spherules per unit weight of sediment may serve as an inverse measure of the rate of sedimentation. Assuming that, in the course of many thousands of years, the chances of a cosmic spherule settling on a unit surface of the ocean floor are about equal all over the planet, their number per unit volume of the deposit should stand in an approximately inverse ratio to the rate of sedimentation. A sediment containing ten times more spherules should accumulate them at a rate ten times less. To the oceanographer, as also to the student of submarine geology, this problem regarding the rate of sedimentation and the age of the deposit found at a certain distance below the bottom surface is of great interest. Once solved, the answer to this question will afford means for *dating* the different volumes of the records of the deep and finding out how many thousand years ago a climatic or a volcanic catastrophe, leaving its traces in the deposit, had occurred.

This reasoning obviously presupposes that the frequency with which the spherules have reached the Earth has remained constant throughout the ages. If this assumption is erroneous, say if the frequency of meteors has varied considerably in the past, the number of spherules per unit volume cannot be expected to give the information desired. On the other hand, if the number of spherules found per unit volume of a homogeneous deposit shows considerable variations from level to level within a long core, these changes may be due to variations in the intensity of the hailstorm of cosmic bullets in the past. Such variations are of great interest to astronomers.

Many years ago a German scientist, Schwinne, suggested that the present rate of meteor falls has an unusually high value owing to our sun with its family of planets having, about 25,000 years ago, run into a cosmic cloud of dust and meteor fragments, after having for a much longer time passed through clearer regions of interstellar space. His main argument was that no fossil meteorites have been discovered in the coal mines, although the total quantity of coal brought up during the last centuries ought to have contained thousands of them. Schwinne's hypothesis of the meteors being derived from cosmic clouds is rejected by many astronomers, and its consequence of limiting meteoric falls to the past 25,000 years is improbable. From what is known about the rate of accumulation of the abyssal sediments, it would mean that the cosmic spherules there should be much rarer, or even non-existent, below a surface layer of about one inch or even less. Anyhow, the problem of how the rate of incidence of meteors into our atmosphere has varied in the past retains its fascination. Since Schwinne's hypothesis was published, the actual frequency of meteors has been studied, especially by astronomers at the Harvard Observatory in Cambridge. Meteor counts made with the naked eye and by means of telescopes have given astonishing values for the total number of shooting stars. Recent figures, published in Watson's excellent book, *Between the Planets,* show that down to the faintest meteors so far studied, over ten thousand million per day enter the atmosphere, and even this figure must be taken as a minimum for the total number. The vast majority of these bullets are extremely small, weighing a fraction of a milligram each, and their size is considerably less than a pinhead. It is only their tremendous energy, transformed into heat and radiant light, which make them observable for a few seconds. None of them reaches the Earth's surface. Instead they are converted into meteoric dust, which slowly settles from great heights, bringing an addition to the surface layers of our planet which eludes direct observation. Watson finds that the total mass of this meteoric dust-rain, including the meteorites actually reaching the Earth in a more or less intact state, is about five metric tons or 5000 kilograms per day.

After the return of the *Albatross,* the problems raised in this chapter were studied in the laboratory. From a long core of red clay from a depth of nearly 2800 fathoms in the central Pacific Ocean, the magnetic particles have been extracted by means of an electromagnetic sieve of high efficiency. The results of this work prove that magnetic spherules are present in variable numbers even down to a depth below the sediment surface of nearly 50 feet, an irrefutable argument against a recent origin.

There is, however, another still more interesting way of studying the accretion of meteoric matter in the abyssal deposits, namely by measuring their content of nickel. Nickel is a very rare element in most terrestrial rocks and continental sediments, and it is almost absent from the ocean waters. On the other hand, it is one of the main components of meteorites, with a percentage varying between one per cent in the stony meteorites up to more than 16 per cent in the metallic meteorites. About two per cent of nickel is assumed to be a fair average for meteorites of all kinds.

Fortunately there are nowadays very accurate methods for measuring minute traces of nickel, sensitive to a few millionths of a gram. By means of such methods, the nickel content has been measured in the long red-clay core mentioned above. The results of these measurements proved the deposit to contain from 0.03 to 0.07 per cent nickel by weight, which is from five to ten times more than in other oceanic sediments of a more rapid rate of accumulation. On the other hand, the rate of growth of the sediment in this particular core has been estimated from radioactive age-determinations to be about half a millimeter or approximately 0.02 inch in one thousand years. Assuming the average nickel content of meteoric dust to be two per cent, an approximate value for the rate of accretion of cosmic dust to the whole Earth can be worked out from these data. The result is very high—about 10,000 tons per day,[1] or over a thousand times higher than the value computed from counting the shooting stars and estimating their mass.

This startling discrepancy between the results found by astronomers counting meteors and our own study of the deep-ocean sediments seemed to throw doubts on the accuracy of our methods. A possible explanation for this apparent contradiction has been furnished by the brilliant work of Dr. Öpik, of the Armagh Observatory, and of Dr. Fred L. Whipple of Harvard. Papers by these

---

[1] This value is, however, an upper limit, as some part of the nickel present in the red clay is probably of terrestrial origin, *i.e.* derived from sea-water or from minerals of deep-sea origin.

scientists show that cosmic dust particles of very small size can pass undamaged through the whole of our atmosphere. Thanks to their relatively large surface, in comparison with their small mass, the frictional heat produced through their encounter with air molecules is dissipated as radiation before the melting-point of the material is reached. Consequently, they are not visible as shooting stars and thus escape direct observation. Dr. Whipple believes that this invisible rain of cosmic dust particles, because of their enormous number, may well give a total weight thousands of times greater than that which the meteor counts have given. In a letter to the author he adds that measurements of nickel and other elements present in the deep-sea deposits appear to be the only way of estimating the total accretion of cosmic matter to our planet. Dr. Öpik has recently sent me a paper on this subject in which he further elaborates his theory of cosmic dust in interplanetary space. According to Öpik, the accretion of cosmic dust on the surface of the Earth may well have values as high as those we have inferred from our analyses of the nickel in deep-sea deposits. He also discusses the possible causes for the large variations in nickel content we have found at different levels in our cores.

Whatever may be the ultimate results from investigations still proceeding regarding the origin of the deep-sea nickel, the whole program gives a striking demonstration of interrelation between different sciences. It is significant that astronomers studying the dust in interplanetary space, which is responsible for the zodiacal light, turn to students of the deep ocean floor for information.

Returning to my seat on the bowsprit of the *Alba-*

tross, to the shooting stars above me and to the living stars beneath me, I am elated as an oceanographer by the thought that they are destined to find their last resting place, as star-dust and as plankton remnants, on the bottom of the deep sea.

Chapter 17

AN AFRICAN INTERLUDE

After the Captain put me ashore in Port Sudan I was stuck. The plane leaving for Cairo next day was fully booked, and the second of the two weekly planes also was crowded. A newly acquired friend, the chief of the airdrome, darkly hinted that "something may happen before Thursday," when the second plane was scheduled to start, but he was annoyed when I innocently asked: "To the plane or to its passengers?"

So with secret joy I settled my mind on an alternative, an inland voyage. I decided to take the Sudan train for Atbara, in order to catch the Khartoum train to Wadi Halfa, and then to sail 200 miles by steamer down the Nile to Shallal. From there I would take the train for Cairo, with a tempting prospect of breaking the journey at Luxor for a day with the dead Pharaohs and in the temple of Amen-Ra.

Some of my new friends at the pleasant Red Sea Hotel in Port Sudan advised me against this plan, intimating that at my ripe age—I was approaching sixty— the heat and lack of comfort on the way might have serious consequences. I assured them that I was so keen on forming a personal acquaintance with the Nile that even if part of the voyage had to be made on the back of a hippopotamus it would not deter me. It appeared that no first-class seats were available, the next semi-weekly train being booked as full as the planes. When I declared myself willing to travel second class, or even third, my friends threw up their hands in horror. My appearing there among the multicolored Fuzzies would be detrimental to the prestige of the White Race, and might even seriously upset the equilibrium of the none-too-stable Sudanese Condominium. My rejoinder, that I had been travelling second class in southern Europe in much less reputable company and without suffering worse than petty thefts, made no impression. My friends were adamant: "It is not done"—the iron curtain behind which unutterable reasons are hidden against the inquisitiveness of unsophisticated foreigners.

However, contacting a friendly local manager of the Sudan Railways, I displayed my impressive Cabinet Passport in which His Majesty the King of Sweden certified that I was travelling on a government mission. In addition, an official telegram from the Swedish Minister in Cairo stating that the Egyptian Government favored my movements, helped me to a first-class compartment all to myself. So I could travel like a gentleman toward my next destination, the Desert and the Nile.

On the sweltering afternoon of May 3rd, our train started slowly to move out of the railway station and up the grade toward the hills, behind which the sun was setting. Diminutive curly-headed Fuzzies, dressed in their innocence and very little else, for a while kept pace with the train, shrilly imploring us to throw coins out of the windows. A white camel was waddling along the line, its long neck undulating gracefully. Its myopic look reminded me of aristocratic spinsters among my acquaintances in Sweden, bowing their way into a crowded concert hall. Seeing these much-abused creatures, one can understand the lyrical outburst of an Arab poet: "Thy gait resembles that of a young camel in springtime."

The landscape gliding slowly past my window became more and more austere the higher we went among the hills, and soon the real desert opened up before me, as a book of fairy tales opens before the eyes of a wondering child.

As I was looking out over the limitless flat sand surface, to which the setting sun lent a delicate peach color, I was strangely reminded of the equally flat and vast surface which we had found right in the center of the Indian Ocean at a depth of more than 2000 fathoms. Will that immense plain ever become lifted out of the deep, and appear before the amazed traveller, ten or perhaps fifty million years from now? And, if so—will there be any traveller, any descendant of our race to see it ... ?

When the sun had set and the stars, as brilliant over the ocean of sand as they were over the water, came out in the sky, and from our seemingly stationary train the night wind from the desert could be heard gently moaning, the beauty of the scenery before me became almost unbearable.

For the hundredth time during this strange voyage around the Earth I thought of my old father, how intensely he would have enjoyed it. He was a great man of science of his day, a pioneer of international oceanography. Moreover, he was an incurable romantic, intensely in love with life and with the mysteries of the Cosmos which, he was firmly convinced, he had been born to unravel. The thought of death was distasteful to him, although personally he had no fears. At the ripe age of over ninety, when he was mentally as active as ever, he once said to me: "What will sustain me in my last moments is an infinite curiosity as to what is to follow." So he became much annoyed with me when I sent him one of my books on popular science, ending with a chapter on the end of the universe, in which I had quoted Swinburne's immortal lines from *The Garden of Proserpine:*

> *From too much love of living,*
> *From hope and fear set free,*
> *We thank with brief thanksgiving*
> *Whatever gods there be*
> *That no life lives forever;*
> *That dead men rise up never;*
> *That even the weariest river*
> *Winds somewhere safe to sea.*

To my father the idea that "no life lives forever" was unacceptable, and the statement that "dead men rise up never" he considered almost as a personal insult.

I was wondering whether he was at that moment looking through my eyes at the loveliness before me, at the majestic desert which he was never to see, just as I may, one day when I have long been dead, look through the eyes of my son at the wonders of the world he will be watching—a mute companion, affectionately remembered in odd moments of retrospection.

For such, according to Science, is the only immortality granted to us, weary wanderers through the desert of life under the starry sky of eternity.

But here I am touching on ultimate things—which,

according to one of my most charming and least articulate English friends, "is not done."

After changing trains at Atbara, we arrived at Wadi Halfa, where the paddle-steamer *Lotus* was waiting to receive us for the Nile voyage. She was a queer-looking vessel, and certainly did not remind me of the lovely lotus flower, but rather of a somewhat bedraggled duck, thanks to her paddle-wheels being far astern. According to one of my fellow-passengers, who was an expert on Nile traffic, she shared with the ducks a taste for diving. In order to counteract such subaqueous tendencies, she had another stern-wheel steamer of smaller size tied alongside her, and the two travelled together in blissful companionship, a mode of navigation which assuredly would have sent our brave Captain of the *Albatross* into a fit. The smaller of the two was reserved for third-class passengers, whose private lives we on the *Lotus* deck, from our more elevated position, could follow in all details.

I got on very well with two of my fellow-passengers who shared the table with me. We dubbed ourselves the Lotus-eaters. One of them, whose generally solemn features were occasionally enlivened by humorous glints, was a charming talker. He turned out to be a great-grand-nephew of the poet Wordsworth and the happy possessor of some priceless manuscripts from those romantic times. His own occupation was somewhat less poetic—making the Sudanese grow cotton and unite in co-operative societies. Our talks ranged from atomic physics to the fertilizing of Sudanese gardens with the clay from ancient tombs. In this connection I was able to refer him to the splendid work of Dr. O. Arrhenius in Sweden on phosphate in the soil as a clue to Bronze Age sites.

The other man was less talkative but equally pleasant, a colonel just retiring from service in the Middle and Far East. Asked how he intended to spend his dignified old age—he was not yet fifty—he intimated that he would like to direct a school of music (military, of course). He was not an active musician, but had a catholic taste, loving Bach, Mozart and Beethoven, and, like myself, cordially detesting Hindemith. I hope he will succeed. Military bands trained in his school could be trusted never to indulge in atonal atrocities, however trying the military situation might become.

A third acquaintance was a missionary who for years had been busy ministering to the heathen of the upper Nile. Realizing that I was a scientist and, consequently, servant of the Devil (perhaps an excusable generalization after the atom bomb), he concentrated his powers of conversion on me. Sitting with him on the deck in the growing dusk, gliding slowly forward on the gray river between walls of desert rock, and with a breeze of more than 100°F. fanning our temples, I felt his vivid description of eternal punishment and the death agonies of stubborn sinners give me a creepy feeling. After a final warning about my meager chances of avoiding still higher temperatures in the future, he left me to my sinister reflections. "A most depressing chap," one of my other friends remarked about him, and I could not help but agree. However, he certainly meant well.

The scenery on both sides of the Nile, once we had passed the narrow bands of vegetation along the shores near Wadi Halfa, is the most austere landscape I have ever seen. The dark brown to almost black color of the splintered rocks, unrelieved by the softer colors of the desert sand, the dwellings on the shores, built of dull gray Nile mud with empty dark holes for windows, the inhabitants slowly moving in front of them arrayed in white or black shrouds, gave an impression of death. We had a feeling of gliding on the River Styx piloted by a Charon who had lost his bearings in an attempt to carry us across. It is possible that the intense preoccupation of the old Egyptians with death, their overwhelming preoccupation with dying instead of living, their toil on enormous pyramids or, later, on vast underground tombs for their dead Pharaohs, may have been inspired by the death-like landscape along their great river.

Arriving at Shallal, our final destination, too late to make a landing on the primitive quay, the captain of our double-duck resolutely ran their joint beaks into the rocky shore, mooring them there overnight—another maneuver which would have upset the captain of the *Albatross*. The temperature in Shallal was high—40°C. or about 106°F. I was told that the annual maximum, which occurs about this time of the year, is 118°F.—a bit of information which I tried to take as refreshing. This was the more advisable, as my ordeal commenced, namely, examination by medical and passport officials. The certificate from our ship's doctor, testifying that I had recently been inoculated against half a dozen mortal maladies, proved to be not valid, since it had not been written on a properly stamped paper. My suggestion that it should be stuck on some Egyptian parchment was received with derision. My Cabinet Passport, flourished before the be-fezzed officer, did not impress him, since it lacked an Egyptian visa. With terror I began to anticipate being detained in Shallal, for a week or more, at a temperature of 106°—or more. But fortunately the Swedish Minister in Cairo had stirred Egyptian officialdom into sending a telegram stating that I should be passed through. After half an hour's search for the telegram, and numerous cups of black coffee, he reluctantly released me.

After a very hot day on board the exhausted *Lotus,* imbibing cooling drinks, my fellow-passengers and I boarded the Cairo train, which had been carefully preheated, having been left in the sun during the whole day. By the judicious use of baksheesh on the guard, I obtained an extremely dusty compartment to myself. Every five minutes he put in his head, suggesting that the baksheesh should be increased on account of the large size of his family. I have a strong impression that Egypt is run mainly on baksheesh; who will supply it in the future, after the English have retired from the country, is a mystery.

At Luxor I got off the train. When it was sliding out from the station I could still hear the sorrowful moaning of the guard: "Baksheesh, baksheesh"—or perhaps it was the engine asthmatically puffing the heavy train into motion. I was triumphantly led away by a host of carriers to the great Luxor Hotel. There the clerk, after carefully running through the ledger, told me that he could give me one double room for one night only. I later discovered that the hotel was practically empty of guests, it being the off season. His exertion, however, naturally demanded an extra shower of baksheesh.

In order to see the wonders of Luxor and its surroundings, it is unfortunately necessary to engage a guide, a profession which I cordially detest. To the hotel clerk I expressed my desire to engage a guide who would undertake to *answer* my questions, but not say a single word unasked. He told me that this was strictly against the nature of a self-respecting guide, and would involve serious risks to his health, wherefore a triple dose of baksheesh had to be expended. Actually the elderly Osman, who took me under his wing for one memorable day, was a miracle. He sat silent unless I asked him questions, to which he gave succinct answers, essentially correct as far as I could judge. His silence was monumental, like the temples we saw—and was none too dearly bought.

It is superfluous to say so, but Luxor *is* a marvel. A still greater marvel is the Valley of the Kings. After crossing the Nile in an ancient boat, we travelled in an age-old carriage, drawn by two mummified horses, which looked as if they had emerged straight from a tomb of the fifteenth dynasty. The experience of descending into these rock-carved tombs—which was done by reflected sunlight, thrown down the vaults by metal mirrors at the entrance—cannot be described.

Tutankhamen, the boy-Pharaoh who died at the age of eighteen, had not had time during his short reign to prepare such sumptuous apartments for his repose as his ancestors had. Barely four chambers of moderate size. Perhaps the small size of his tomb had caused it to be overlooked by robbers during the thirty centuries which have passed since his burial. When Howard Carter found the tomb, just as he had decided to give up the search, all its treasures were still undisturbed. They are now the pride of the Museum in Cairo. Only the mummy of the king has been piously left in its stone sarcophagus under a heavy protecting sheet of glass.

Of late the Valley of the Kings has been supplied with electricity, so that during the tourist season one can see the interiors of the tombs, brightly lit by electric bulbs. Fortunately the current is shut off during the hot season.

I therefore had the privilege of seeing the underground miracles by the romantic light of candles, carried by my excellent guide. It was a sight never to be forgotten.

From the Valley of the Kings our two equine mummies drew us back toward Thebes to inspect the temple built by the great Hatshepsut, the Queen Elizabeth of Egypt. She sent her fleet exploring the coast of East Africa and, incidentally, made her neighbors as well as her own relatives decidedly uncomfortable. Anyhow, her taste in architecture was above reproach. Later in the day I had occasion to admire the small temple which she had added to the gigantic temple of Amen-Ra. We also paid our respects to the broken giant statue of Rameses II, lying among the mighty pillars of his temple. Returning to the Nile, we again crossed the river in our rickety boat, and Osman was dismissed until the afternoon. I expect that his family was inundated with the pent-up talk he had been forbidden in my company.

The afternoon's drive out to Sakhara, to the temple of Amen-Ra, was windy, sandy and lengthy, but certainly worthwhile. I have never seen anything even approaching in grandeur this temple, dedicated to the Sun-God, to which Pharaoh after Pharaoh had added minor temples and wings of his own. Perhaps the most impressive sight there is the forest of pillars in the wing of Rameses VI, 138 in all, according to the truthful Osman. The very work of laying bare these giant pillars from the layers of soil accumulated around them in the course of three thousand years must have been a heavy task, even with the aid of modern tools of excavation.

As a curious example of the contrast between the chronology of the human race and of the ocean floor, it struck me that during the thirty-odd centuries which have passed since this stupendous temple of the Sun-God was built, the red clay in the Central Pacific Ocean has not increased in thickness by more than about one-tenth of an inch. What will remain of our Machine Age, recognizable to posterity, after another tenth of an inch has been added to the same deposit?

Returning to Luxor late in the afternoon, when the temple ruins were magically illuminated by the sunset, I imprudently paid a visit to the antique dealers. I left them with an almost empty wallet, but carried with me: (a) the favorite alabaster flower-pot of the great Queen Hatshepsut; (b) a necklace which had once adorned the lovely bosom of Queen Nefertiti; (c) a scarabaeus used by Tutankhamen for signing his love-letters to that lady during their engagement. I would fain also have bought the drinking-goblet of Rameses II, but was unfortunately short of cash. To my agreeable surprise, the customs officials in Cairo made no objection to my carrying off these priceless antiquities to Sweden.

On a Sunday morning I arrived in Cairo, and drove straight to Shepheard's Hotel with the same feeling of pride as when, in my younger days, I had, like a Count of Monte Cristo, drawn my first million on the Rothschild Bank in Vienna. For in Shepheard's Hotel, according to detective stories, all international spies, all bewitching adventuresses and all smugglers of heroin, diamonds and Egyptian antiquities are housed, watched over by lynx-eyed detectives. On the occasion of my visit, the company was decidedly tamer, in fact depressingly so. But the hotel was grand, the service perfect, and the word "baksheesh" was not even heard within its hallowed precincts.

Fortunately, I saw the Cairo Museum of Antiquities in the morning; it closed at 2 P.M. and remained closed also on the following day. There I saw and marvelled at the treasures from Tutankhamen's tomb which I had visited the preceding day—marvelled, not so much at the profusion of gold, which is said to represent about half a million pounds in value, but at the exquisite workmanship of the inlaid chests, the benches, the alabaster heads decorating the sacred urns, not to speak of the jewelry. The perfection in taste and the striking design have hardly been rivalled even during the Italian Renaissance.

The homeward flight via London proved to be a more complicated affair than I had expected. The plane in which I had booked a seat failed to turn up, having been delayed by a storm on its eastward flight. Again, thanks to the kind help of the Swedish Minister, I obtained instead a seat in a fast plane from Johannesburg, which brought me to London in sixteen hours instead of thirty. The extra day I could spend in London was used to the full in getting in touch with the Hydrographic Department of the Admiralty, the Swedish Institute in London, and several eminent men of science. Finally, on an afternoon in the middle of May, my plane for Göteborg took off. Three hours later the rocky coast of Sweden spread below us, and the lights from my own city twinkled through the spring night like the jewels in the tiara of a dead queen of ancient Egypt.

Chapter 18

CRUISING IN THE MEDITERRANEAN

In many respects the Mediterranean is an ideal field of work for students of oceanography and of submarine geology. During the greater part of the year the weather there is fine, the swell moderate, and conditions of visibility perfect. Moreover, fairly great depths—from 1000 to 2000 fathoms—are within short distances of excellent harbors. Finally, the bottom of the Mediterranean affords special interest through the occurrence there of coarse-grained layers interlined in the fine-grained sediments. Whether these layers are of continental origin —*i.e.* desert sand blown seaward by strong gales—or organic remains from outbursts of intense plankton production, or volcanic ash from eruptions of the numerous volcanoes of the region, their study is of great interest.

In 1946, during our preliminary cruise in the western Mediterranean in the *Skagerak*, we raised long cores which contained a considerable number of coarse-grained layers. Especially in the Tyrrhenian Sea—where their origin was largely from volcanoes on the mainland (especially from Mt. Vesuvius and its predecessor Mt. Somma)—the number and thickness of such ash-layers increased toward the lower end of the core, indicating a greater volcanic activity in the past. Attempts to attribute the topmost layers in these cores to historical eruptions of Vesuvius didn't end in conclusive results because of the difficulty experienced in comparing the volcanic mineral fragments found in the cores with those from the immediate vicinity of the volcano. With due reservations about the correctness of the identifications, I offer here schematic representations of vertical sections from three cores, taken on a line from the Bay of Naples toward the Sardinian coast. The ash-layers marked A.D. 79 in cores 15 and 13—the latter raised from a depth of 2000 fathoms near the center of the Tyrrhenian Sea—would correspond to the terrific outbreak which covered the Roman cities of Pompeii and Herculaneum under deep layers of volcanic ash and mud, thus preserving unique products of Roman civilization to our day. (See Fig. 4.)

The raising of long cores from the eastern Mediterranean, especially near the south coast of Crete, was one of the objectives on our *Albatross* program. Just before the expedition left Suez, I received a letter from an eminent American archaeologist strongly urging us to take as many, and as long, cores as possible within the eastern Mediterranean, in order to link up data from submarine geology with those from archaeology.

Dr. Kullenberg, in my temporary absence from the *Albatross*, was in charge of the scientific work on board, and he undertook to carry out this request as far as possible. Before that, he devoted several days to core-sampling at moderate depths off the Nile delta. It seemed possible that long cores taken there might reach down to layers deposited during an earlier, rainier climatic period, when the sediment deposited by the great river could be expected to reveal signs of those conditions and give data about the transition from moist to arid climate over North Africa. But the high rate of sedimentation near the coast—where the deposition of the finer sediment particles is accelerated through contact between the brackish river-water and underlying sea-water of high salinity—made this effort unsuccessful. On the other hand, Jerlov's studies by optical methods of the suspended particles in the different water-layers gave a very clear picture of the processes of water-mixing and sedimentation in this interesting region.

Since the famous excavations on Crete by Sir Arthur Evans, we know that this island was a center of commerce, of seafaring, and of a highly developed civilization as early as the beginning of the second millennium B.C. This Middle-Minoan culture was partially destroyed about the year 1600 B.C., an event which Evans attributes to a seismic catastrophe laying the palaces in ruins.

On the island arc which stretches from Attica to the coast of Asia Minor there are several volcanoes, the best known of them being Santorin, situated about sixty nautical miles north of Crete. Santorin has had several eruptions in modern times, generally accompanied by more or less intense earthquakes. None of these, nor the earlier outbreaks in historical times, can be compared with a terrific catastrophe about the middle of the second millennium B.C. A great part of the island of Santorin then caved in, and prehistoric dwellings on the island which have been excavated in modern times were buried under a layer of pumice nearly one hundred feet thick.

It seems natural to ascribe the destruction of the Minoan palaces at Knossos to intense earthquakes heralding or accompanying this sudden unleashing of the subterranean forces. But certain writers have recently put forward the suggestion that the clouds of volcanic ash thrown skyward by the outbreak may have been spread across the eastern Mediterranean by the prevailing northerly winds, and reached the lower Nile. In that case, the "Egyptian darkness," the ninth of the plagues with which the Lord smote Pharaoh and his subjects in order to make them release the children of Israel from bondage, might have had its origin in the eruption of Santorin. From the somewhat hazy Biblical chronology, this catastrophe has been dated at about 1500 B.C., about a century later than the archaeological dating of the catastrophe at Knossos. Considering the vagueness of the events related in Genesis, the slight discrepancy in date need not be taken too seriously.

Can any trace of a similar ash-rain be found in the *Albatross* cores, taken in the vicinity of Crete? As a matter of fact, several of these cores have a distinct layer of volcanic ash, some of them even two layers, of which one occurs at levels between 80 and 170 cm. below the sediment surface, different in different cores, but obviously due to the same ash-rain spread over a wide area. Ascribing to this ash-rain the age at which archaeologists have arrived for the prehistoric Santorin catastrophe, say about 1600 B.C., the thirty-five centuries or so which have since elapsed correspond to rates of sedimentation for the different cores ranging from 20 to 40 cm. in a thousand years, values which are quite plausible for the eastern Mediterranean. If this estimate is confirmed through investigations still proceeding, it would mean that archaeology may help submarine geochronology, assistance which perhaps will be repaid in coming years. There is no doubt that extensive sampling of long cores from the Aegean Sea may give valuable contributions to the knowledge of this part of the Mediterranean which has been especially turbulent not only from a political but also from a volcanological and a seismological point of view. According to current geological theories, the Aegean Sea is of very recent origin, caused by a local breakdown of the uppermost crust of the Earth. If this is true, its birth and the later subsidence of its bottom may be revealed in the stratifications of very long cores taken at representative points. They may also give evidence regarding the climatic changes which are assumed to have occurred after the end of the last of the Ice Age, twenty to twenty-five thousand years ago. No doubt the very rough bottom profile characteristic of this lunar landscape will prove a complication. Nevertheless, parts of the sea bottom with fairly undisturbed sediments are likely to occur, where investigations both by coring and by submarine explosions may yield results of very great interest. This also applies to the Sea of Candia between Santorin and the north coast of Crete, where the ash-layer from the great outbreak about 1600 B.C. could be identified.

The cruise of the *Albatross* through the region near Malta and Sicily and into the Tyrrhenian Sea, where the *Skagerak* in 1946 had raised its longest core, also yielded a number of cores of considerable importance on this second attempt. Here in the center of the Tyrrhenian Sea the *Albatross* raised a core of record length —19 meters, or more than 60 feet. Here also there were numerous interstratifications of coarse sediments with fine clay. These are at present being examined by well-known specialists in geology and mineralogy.

In investigating the Tyrrhenian cores, a technique not previously used in deep-sea research has been applied—the pollen-analytical method. Largely thanks to the work of Swedish authorities—Sernander, von Post, and others—pollen grains from trees, bushes and plants, which are surprisingly well preserved under water, have been used for chronological purposes. Provided a "pollen-analytical key" is available, *i.e.* a systematic survey of how vegetation has varied during many thousands of years, it is possible to date a certain layer from the relative frequency of the different pollen grains found in it.

A close examination of the three cores taken from the *Skagerak* in the Tyrrhenian Sea showed that they contain quite a number of recognizable pollen grains, largely from conifers, which had been carried out over the sea surface from forests on the Italian mainland and on Sardinia. The number of such pollen grains found in different layers of the cores varied considerably with depth, indicating changes in the composition of the forests, which have no doubt been caused by corresponding changes in the climate. For lack of a detailed pollen-analytical key valid for the coasts of the Tyrrhenian Sea, no very definite conclusions have as yet been drawn from this preliminary study. Material now being investigated by specialists may, we hope, give a clearer picture of these changes, which, in turn, will be a valuable help in interpreting the geochronology of the western Mediterranean.

Chapter 19

FROM MONACO TO THE CAPE VERDE
ISLANDS

For twenty years, around 1900, the small principality of Monaco was a world center for deep-sea research. Its sovereign, Prince Albert I of the House of Grimaldi, devoted the active years of his life and a great part of his revenues to oceanographic investigations. He assembled a staff of distinguished scientists and supported their work liberally. He built four ocean-going research yachts, of increasing tonnage and improved equipment, and made long cruises both in the Mediterranean and in adjacent parts of the North Atlantic Ocean. His favorite field for work which he, ironically, used to call "my kingdom," was the submarine platform—rich in deeps, shoals and interesting bottom deposits—which supports the Azores. Besides physical oceanography, in which he carried out valuable research, the Prince was passionately interested in hunting the big game of the ocean, the sperm whales. Having observed that these giants have a special taste for the large octopuses which live in great depths and therefore are rarely caught, he used these whales as collectors for his Museum. From the stomachs of freshly harpooned whales he extricated the remnants of their last meal. By this means he salvaged a unique specimen of a giant squid called *Lepidotheutis grimaldii,* one of the greatest treasures of the *Musée Océanographique* in Monaco.

This magnificent Museum, built of dazzlingly white limestone on the very summit of the Monaco Rock, may well be called a Palace of the Sea. It contains unique instruments and tools of research, illuminating the development of the science of the sea from its earliest days. There are splendid exhibits of subaqueous life, of useful marine products and animals, from fur-seals, walruses and sea-elephants to tortoise-shell trinkets, mother-of-pearl, red corals and amber. The beautiful aquarium of the *Musée Océanographique* has also become a great attraction to tourists. In addition there are a fine library, workshops and a number of well-equipped laboratories for research.

Prince Albert also founded both the renowned Institute of Oceanography in Paris and a museum in Monaco for the prehistoric finds made in the Grimaldi Cave near the Italian frontier, where skeletons of Cro-Magnon people of giant stature were discovered. The Prince also sponsored the famous Monaco Map, on which all the important bathymetric features of the three oceans are set out. Its third revised edition is now being issued from the office of the International Hydrographic Bureau, which is located in Monaco.

On a windy day, May 28, 1948, Monaco saw the stately hull and the four tall masts of the *Albatross,* gaily beflagged, drawing near. With a graceful curtsey for each wave, the ship passed through the narrow entrance into the harbor and reached its berth, which had been reserved just outside the building of the International

Hydrographic Bureau. Among the expectant crowd waiting on the quay there were a number of Swedes, mainly the wives of the officers and staff of the *Albatross,* who had come to spend a few days with their husbands after a separation of nearly eleven months. Dr. Nybelin of the Natural History Museum of Göteborg and Professor Weibull of the Bofors Armament Works, who was to accompany us to Tangier, were among the arrivals, and so were our generous patrons Major and Mrs. Herbert Jacobsson.

Our reception was memorable, both by the officials of Monaco and of the Museum, led by its director Commandant Rouch. His Highness Prince Louis, the son of Albert, gave a lunch in his picturesque castle, and his ministers of State, like the mayor of Monaco, vied with each other in offering us hospitality. The opportunity of visiting the Museum was eagerly seized, not only by the scientists and the officers of the *Albatross,* but also by the crew, including the young apprentices, as were the many other places of interest and amusement with which the lovely Côte d'Azur is so well provided.

On June 4th, after a delightful but not exactly restful week, we left this Mecca of Oceanography, heading southwest for Gibraltar and the Atlantic Ocean. Before our departure we had a chance to show our ship and her equipment to representative guests from the Museum and from the Hydrographic Bureau, the latter including one British and one American admiral. A representative of the *Discovery* Expedition, Dr. Herdman, had come expressly from London to Monaco in order to see our gear in operation. In spite of a fresh mistral blowing, which made the sea off Monaco uncomfortably choppy, Kullenberg succeeded in raising a 40-foot core.

Weibull dropped depth-charges and had their echoes recorded—in all, a highly satisfactory demonstration. A film taken on board at the time was afterward shown in the cinemas of three continents.

After touching for two days at Tangier where, to our great regret, Weibull had to leave the expedition for Sweden, our Atlantic venture was resumed. During that cruise, biological research at great depths by means of the trawl was one of the main purposes. Thanks to experience accumulated from deep-sea coring during the preceding year, and thanks also to the expert handling of the deep-sea winch by Kullenberg and Jonasson, this rather difficult technique was mastered and we had a large degree of success. But serious complications were not lacking. One of these—which inevitably arises during trawling—was the severe twisting of the steel cable. This made it very difficult to operate the coring-tube afterward, because of its tendency to rotate rapidly as the steel cable unwound itself. Another difficulty was the highly irregular profile of the Atlantic bottom at great depths, which often made trawling precarious and at times impossible. Thanks to the echo-graph, we were forewarned when the bottom became too rough. Even so, accidents sometimes happened, leading to damage or even to a complete loss of our precious trawl. In spite of all this, a number of very deep hauls were successfully carried out and Nybelin had the joy of collecting a rich harvest of the fantastic organisms which inhabit the great depths below the 2000-fathom line.

The long cores of sediment raised between Tangier and the Cape Verde Islands were quite interesting. Grains of sand with rounded-off edges, indicating an origin from the deserts of northwest Africa, were of common occurrence. It is a not unusual experience for sailing ships in these regions to have their sails colored brownish red by fine dust grains blown seaward by gales, sometimes as far out as halfway across to the coast of South America. In some cores there were even compact layers of sand in certain levels, which are not quite easy to explain, unless "turbidity currents" along a sloping bottom are assumed. In a core taken to the southwest of the Canary Islands from a depth exceeding 1600 fathoms, we found coarse fragments of calcareous shells. It is not clear how these shells, obviously products of a much shallower water fauna, could have become transported so far out from any coast or island. A large subsidence of the ocean floor in this highly unstable region of the Earth's crust can't be considered impossible.

Some of the calcareous cores taken from this cruise have, since the return of the expedition, been analyzed in Göteborg by a German authority on *foraminifera*, Dr. W. Schott. His conclusions, which are about to be published, indicate that considerable variations in the water temperature must have occurred during the late Quaternary Age, with distinct effects on the composition of the plankton inhabiting the surface layers. This agrees well with the results of his earlier study of the cores from our first Atlantic crossing a year before, and also with the results obtained by Dr. Phleger from his analysis of a long core from the Caribbean Sea.

On Midsummer Day, June 24, 1948, the *Albatross* reached the harbor of São Vicente, among the Cape Verde Islands, the color of which belies their name. Normally these islands are largely desert-like, a state aggravated by a severe drought of long standing which reduced what little vegetation there was to sorry remnants. Our doctor had set his heart on a botanical excursion to the neighboring island of Santo Antão, where water is less scarce. But all our attempts to elicit from the Portuguese authorities the necessary permission for sending a boat over to Santo Antão for botanical studies failed. Visitors to that island were evidently not welcomed by the Portuguese. The conclusion we felt forced to draw from this refusal was sinister. Probably the drought, lack of provisions and of medical care had affected its population to such an extent that their destitute state was not desirable publicity. Eriksson and Nybelin therefore had to limit their biological studies to the shore fauna off São Vicente, which is interesting enough and had so far not suffered from the water shortage.

São Vicente is not a very cheerful place even at its best. In fact it seemed to us the most dismal island we had visited during the whole cruise. After delivering and receiving our mail, and with such provisions as were available brought on board, we set sail again, heading for the Equator and our next field of work, the mysterious Romanche Deep, one of the most interesting parts of the bottom of the equatorial Atlantic Ocean.

PLATE 25

YOUNG BOOBIES ON
ST. PAUL'S ROCKS

J. Eriksson

H. Pettersson

THE MOST DESOLATE SPOT IN THE ATLANTIC OCEAN

PLATE 26

A SHARK WITH *REMORA* ATTACHED

J. Eriksson

SCARLET-COLOURED DEEP-SEA PRAWNS

PLATE 27

R. Pettersson

OUR LARGEST
DEEP-SEA FISH

THE LARGE
DREDGE BROUGHT
ON BOARD

J. Eriksson

PLATE 28

J. Eriksson

JERLOV ATTENDING TO THE BATHYTHERMOGRAPH

LARGE SAMPLER FOR RADIUM ANALYSIS

Chapter 20

TO THE ROMANCHE DEEP AND
ST. PAUL'S ROCKS

Pessimists assert that in a remote future all water will disappear from the surface of our planet, having been converted into chemical compounds with its rocks. Our Earth will then resemble its neighbor in space, the desert planet Mars, which already has reached an extreme state of desiccation. In that remote future, all the oceans will vanish and oceanographers become extinct.[1] Let us partly anticipate this dismal state by assuming that about half the water masses contained in our oceans has disappeared, which will make their surface fall by a lit-

[1] As is nearly always the case in geophysical science, a diametrically opposite view has been propounded by some geologists, namely that the water, instead of disappearing *into* the crust, has been produced *from* it as "magmatic" water, released at volcanic outbreaks. This view, more cheering to oceanographers than the desiccation hypothesis, implies that the water content of the oceans has been steadily growing for hundreds of millions of years and may ultimately swamp the continents, thus reducing geographers to the same regrettable lack of occupation as would be the case with oceanographers according to the opposite view. The author need not state which of these two alternatives appears to him the more attractive. Moreover, the drying up of the waters would imply the appearance of a new mid-Atlantic continent and a rabid international contest for its possession—a political consequence one shudders to contemplate.

tle over 2000 fathoms. The Atlantic Ocean will then have less than half its present extent and, moreover, be split up into two "demi-Atlantics" separated by an entirely new mid-Atlantic continent, the present submarine Atlantic Ridge. Just below the Equator, where this ridge runs from east to west and has its narrowest part, there will be a channel dividing the new Atlantis into a northern and a southern part.

Actually, the submarine channel corresponding to this future strait has never been sounded, but its existence has been inferred from the water temperature near the bottom on both sides of the ridge. The contrast found there can be explained only by an influx into the eastern Atlantic valley from the western valley, where the bottom temperature is lowered by the steady northward flow of the Antarctic bottom current with its almost ice-cold water. Here, in the immediate vicinity of the hypothetical Romanche Channel, one finds one of the most curious formations of the whole ocean floor, the Romanche Deep, discovered in 1883 by the French surveying ship *La Romanche*. Quite close to the ridge, where the depth is less than 1500 fathoms, the mechanical soundings from the *Romanche* gave the astounding depth of 4030 fathoms, or 7370 meters.

This altogether unprecedented depth—for all other great ocean depths are found close to continental coasts or near island festoons—was for many years regarded with skepticism. Finally, in 1901, its existence was confirmed by a sounding close to the previous position by the German expedition ship *Gauss*, which obtained practically the same results. In addition, the *Gauss* managed to raise from this hole in the sea bottom a sediment core which showed an extraordinary stratification over its length of 25 inches, indicating that great changes in the conditions, presumably also in the total depth, had taken place fairly recently.

The equatorial strip of the Atlantic Ocean between longitudes 15°W. and 30°W. is known for the frequency of sea-tremors reported from ships crossing it. Evidently the sea bottom there is a zone of pronounced instability in the Earth's crust, where structural or volcanic forces are active, so that abrupt vertical displacements of the bottom, or submarine landslides down the steep slopes of the mid-Atlantic Ridge, are likely to occur.

From the first, a visit to the Romanche Deep with our long core-samplers, capable of raising cores thirty to forty times as long as those obtained from the *Gauss,* had formed a salient point in my plans for the expedition. On our way south from São Vicente, a number of interesting cores were raised by Kullenberg, and Nybelin—who had joined the expedition in Monaco—made successful hauls with the 30-foot trawl in depths between 2000 and 3000 fathoms. His catches included several extremely rare fish and invertebrate organisms from great depths. Once completely analyzed by specialists, they will greatly increase our meager knowledge of the strange fauna of the ice-cold water over the deepest regions of the ocean floor.

When the *Albatross* crossed the Equator—for the seventeenth time during our cruise—the season was so far advanced that the equatorial water surface was wholly under the sway of the southeast trade wind, which set up a fairly swift current from the south-southeast. Neither wind nor current was favorable to our undertaking, which was to sound the Romanche Deep and, if possible, to raise long cores from its mysterious sediments. Our Captain navigated the *Albatross* with consummate skill and took very exact astronomical observations—as often as the generally overcast sky permitted. Thanks to him, our zigzag course during the three days and nights devoted to the Romanche Deep could be plotted on the chart with considerable accuracy. The wind, waves and swell were not favorable for our echo-sounder which, therefore, did not draw continuous profiles across the Romanche Deep. In order to determine the water depth, we had repeatedly to lay the ship to and stop the diesel engine, because its oscillations disturbed the echo recording.

In spite of these difficulties, we were able to confirm the work of our predecessors, and, in addition, to find —some ten nautical miles to the west-south-west of their position—a still greater depth of 4175 fathoms, or 7640 meters, thus beating the *Romanche* sounding made in 1883 by nearly 150 fathoms. Only twelve miles to the southwest of this record deep we reached the slope of the mid-Atlantic Ridge, which rose to a minimum depth of only 2600 meters. This represents an average incline of almost 1:4, comparable with the steep grades in the Swiss Alps.

Although the irregular profile of the bottom was not favorable for making soundings, we obtained a core nearly 47 feet long with pronounced stratification, indicating considerable changes in the local conditions of sedimentation in the past. The uppermost layers were dark in color with almost black streaks, containing a large admixture of humus from decomposed organic matter. Farther down, the color of the sediment was a light gray, and it contained a fair quantity of calcareous shells, whereas 20 feet from the top of the core there was sand and globigerina shells with underlying bands of alternating light and dark color. The final interpretation of this remarkable core must be left for a complete stratigraphic analysis, which is now under way.

The result from a second attempt at coring at this great depth was even more sensational. Here the heavy core-sampler was abruptly stopped by a layer of coarse sand mixed with sediment, so that the total length obtained was only about six feet. The mineralogical investigation in the sand can be expected to give information regarding the material from which the Atlantic Ridge has been built up. It does not seem improbable that, in a geologically recent past, the highest parts of the ridge may have protruded above the ocean surface. A comparison with the minerals from the only remaining part of the equatorial Atlantic Ridge still above water, St. Paul's Rocks, may give the necessary information.

We had included a visit to the desolate St. Paul's Rocks in our program. The advanced season and the heavy swell at first made it doubtful that a landing could be made there without considerable risk to our life-boat. Our luck held, however, and we, the landing-party, were brought safely into the small horseshoe bight on the leeward side of the group. Our eight sturdy oarsmen pulled bravely against the long Atlantic swell, while the *Albatross* kept at a respectful distance off the breakers.

A great cloud of seabirds, sole inhabitants of the rocks, rose and hovered over our heads, hailing our arrival with indignant cries accompanied by a remarkably effective form of aerial bombing. To our agreeable surprise, the landing proved much easier than it had appeared from afar. There was no need to swim for the shore, which was perhaps just as well, considering the throng of eager and probably hungry sharks which expectantly crowded around the boat, viciously snapping at our oars. The main island, about 300 feet long, on which we landed—the other islands were inaccessible because of the swell and the sharks—had the remnants of a small lighthouse on its highest rock, which is snow-white from the droppings of innumerable birds. Most of these birds, boobies and two kinds of terns, calmly stayed on their nests, but many were up in the air attacking us from above with their hard beaks. They were absolutely fearless. The boobies were busy feeding their chicks, woolly snow-white creatures, with flying fish they had caught in the sea and which they disgorged for the benefit of their offspring. We had excellent opportunities for photographing bird-life and studying their nests as well as their eggs and chicks.

Besides the birds, there were fascinating specimens of marine life in crystal-clear pools scattered among the rocks. In one of these I happened to light on a fairly large octopus and managed to capture him and bring him back to the ship for our collection. But I had a tough fight with that wilful clamminess, as Victor Hugo describes the giant octopus in his immortal *Travailleurs de la Mer*. The most interesting object on the island was the rock itself. It is an ultrabasic rock from a deeper layer of the Earth's crust, which has emerged through enormous fissures in the ocean floor, building up the Atlantic Ridge during millions upon millions of years. It has been strongly eroded by wave action and, in consequence, presents fantastic formations, increasing the picturesqueness of these strange islands. One interesting point will be to measure their content of radium, which, according to prevalent ideas about ultrabasic rocks, should be very low, but where surprises are not altogether improbable.

In spite of its loneliness, its barren rocks and unfriendly shore-line, there is a queer fascination about this little island group, where landings are very rare. Its position, right on the ship lane from Europe to South American harbors, make the islands dangerous to navigation. For this reason the Brazilian Government, to which they belong, mounted an automatic light-beacon of the famous Swedish Aga type, some fifteen years ago, on the highest rock. After a severe earthquake, it went out of action and now stands useless and empty save for nesting terns. With pangs of regret we watched this small token of civilization and the desolate rock it crowns disappear beneath the blue horizon as our *Albatross* ploughed Westward Ho! The last we saw was a cloud of seabirds still hovering over it.

Chapter 21

FISHING AT GREAT DEPTHS

It is a common illusion that, compared with the green Earth, the Sea is relatively barren as a producer of the necessities of life. Indeed, in earlier, more religious centuries, it was considered that it would have been an incomprehensible oversight of the Creator if, when he divided the waters from the solid earth, he had accorded more space to the ocean than to the land. Mainly for this reason, and also to safeguard the stability of the globe, a vast hypothetical Terra Australis was assumed to occupy the higher southern latitudes.

Only about a century ago did scientists begin to realize the astounding fertility of the oceans. By means of the silk net and the microscope the minute plants in the surface layers—the so-called phyto-plankton—were recognized and studied. These unicellular drifting algae, a few thousandths of an inch in diameter, energized by submarine daylight, are producers of the organic matter from which the basic foodstuff of the ocean is built up. In northern waters, during a few weeks of early spring, their number increases from some hundred cells per cubic centimeter of water up to a million or even more.

Their rate of production is then so high per acre of sea-surface that it can well compare with that of an equally large potato-field in summer. From this production a whole hierarchy of animal life—beginning with minute animals, zoa-plankton—derives its nourishment, with the fish, the seals, the whales and the sea-birds as a super-structure. From these, humanity obtains its sea-food to a value of several billion pounds annually. For all this bounty our thanks are due to the microscopic grass on the meadows of the sea and to the daylight penetrating into the waters which sustain them. An important consequence is that the main productivity of the sea is located in the surface layers, where submarine daylight retains an intensity sufficient for maintaining the photosynthesis of the algae. Dwellers in the dark depths of the ocean have to live on the crumbs falling from the table spread in the upper layers. Another remarkable consequence is that, in contrast to the continents, where plant and animal life abound in the lower latitudes and the polar regions are nearly sterile, the ocean is most fertile in the far north and south. There the physical and chemical conditions in the surface layers are much more favorable to microscopic plant life than near the Equator. Hence the vast shoals of cod, herring and mackerel visiting the coasts in higher latitudes. Hence also the giant whales, now, alas, almost extinct, which feed on enormous swarms of small shrimp-like organisms near or beyond the polar circles.

From a commercial point of view, fishing at great depths has no importance. But science has an absorbing interest in the rare deep-sea organisms which are able to exist under extremely high water-pressure, at the low temperature of the ice-cold bottom water and in the complete darkness prevailing near the ocean floor. Only a century ago, most biologists were prepared to endorse the statement of the great Edward Forbes that at a depth of about 300 fathoms runs a zero-line of animal life and that greater depths are uninhabitable. During the next decades, however, evidence obtained by dredging at increasing depths for sea animals disproved this. Gradually the zero-line of marine life was pushed farther and farther down, until the results of the *Challenger* Expedition of 1872-76 proved that even at depths of 3000 fathoms there exists a fauna of bottom-living invertebrate organisms.

For lack of adequate gear, fish from such great depths are much more difficult to catch than those dwelling near the surface. One of the great triumphs of the late Prince Albert of Monaco was his record haul near the equatorial Atlantic in the beginning of this century, when he managed to bring up star-fish and one fish from a depth of nearly 3300 fathoms.

Fishing at great depths meets with enormous technical difficulties. The trawl which is so efficient in scouring the bottom of the North Sea for fish requires steel cables of great strength and a corresponding weight. As long as the depth does not exceed a few hundred fathoms, this is not difficult; but at depths five to ten times greater, the length and weight of the trawling cable become almost prohibitive and so does the strain on the winch used for working it. Two cables, one for each wing of the commercial trawls, can be used at moderate depths. But at greater depths one must trust to luck that the trawl is not turned upside down as it reaches the bottom on its one cable. Moreover, with a given length of cable which, according to its obliquity, has to exceed the total depth by one-third or more, there is always the risk that the trawl may not remain in contact with the bottom during the haul or else may bury itself in the sediment. In either case there is little chance of any catch, and in the latter case considerable risk of breaking or even losing the trawl. Finally, with an uneven bottom such as often occurs at great ocean depths, there is the additional danger of the trawl getting torn against a rock or against a steep upward slope of the bottom.

Since the *Albatross* was provided for the coring work with a powerful electrically-driven winch and with steel cables of great length, it seemed very tempting, when planning the expedition, to include trawlings at great depths in its program. For various reasons this plan had to be postponed until the three concluding months of the cruise, when the North Atlantic down to the Equator was to be our field of work. As already mentioned, Dr. Nybelin undertook to direct the biological work, for which purpose he joined the expedition at Monaco. During the preceding eleven months of coring at great depths, considerable experience had been gained in working the new winch with long steel cables, experience which proved most valuable in deep trawling. Moreover, Kullenberg, to whose supervision of the winch work much of our success was due, had by mathematical analysis and experiments made on board worked out the exact length of cable required to keep the trawl in contact with the bottom at a given depth and with a given speed of the ship.

A great asset in this work was our recording echo-sounder, by means of which, under favorable conditions of wind and swell, a detailed bottom profile was drawn. Thanks to this, we could pick out beforehand a suitable field of work with a fairly even bottom and, reversing our course, tow the trawl along it, keeping a continuous control of the depth at which it was moving, some two to three nautical miles behind the ship. The low power of our diesel engines was a drawback. The drag involved in towing between 3000 and 6000 fathoms of steel cable, plus the trawl, slowed the speed of the ship to one and a half to two knots. This was in general adequate in a smooth sea with no strong surface current running. But against wind and swell, and especially in a strong current, the movement of the trawl along the bottom became so slow that our chances of a catch became meager. Considering these and other difficulties, Nybelin's results, some of which are here summarized, must be considered surprisingly good.

The first haul, made to the north of the Canary Islands at a depth of 2350 fathoms, was successful. No fewer than twelve bottom-living fish, belonging to six different species, were caught. In addition, the trawl brought up a number of invertebrate bottom organisms, including a quaint-looking white crustacean with red eyes related to the genus *Munidopsis*. Added to this catch of abyssal animals, there were a number of deep-water prawns and fish which happened to get caught in the trawl as it was hauled through the intermediate water layers. At the smaller second haul, made farther south, three bottom fish were brought up from nearly 2700 fathoms.

The third haul, made in over 3000 fathoms over a bottom covered with red clay, was a tremendous find. No fewer than 22 bottom fish belonging to six different species were caught, including the extremely rare *Grimaldichtys profundissimus,* of which the only previously known specimen had been caught by Prince Albert of Monaco in his record haul from 3300 fathoms. In addition, there were several different species of holothurians, star-fish and 63 specimens of brittle-stars, besides a number of deep-sea animals, with squids predominating.

A fourth haul of particular interest was made at a depth of nearly 3000 fathoms close to the famous Romanche Channel just below the Equator. Besides six bottom fish, the catch included over a score of the so-called "street lamps of the abyss" of the genus *Umbellula*, each with its tuft of phosphorescent colonies at the top of a long stalk rising several feet above the sea bottom. This sea-pen normally thrives only in moving water, and its presence therefore affords an interesting confirmation of the hypothetical bottom current assumed to flow through the Romanche Channel from the western Atlantic valley into the eastern, carrying nearly ice-cold water from the Antarctic bottom current. (See Fig. 11.)

The most sensational of Nybelin's hauls was that made to the north of the Virgin Islands at a depth of between 4200 and 4400 fathoms, with a total length of nearly 40,000 feet of steel cable paid out. The catch, although very meager, gave definite proof that at this enormous depth living bottom organisms exist, namely, small sea-cucumbers of the *Peniagone* species and also worms, isopods and amphipods. This means that the realm of life extends at least 1000 fathoms deeper than the limit reached by Prince Albert of Monaco with his record haul mentioned earlier.

Among other catches made during the homeward cruise across the North Atlantic Ocean was our largest deep-sea fish, *Nematonurus armatus* with a length of nearly 27 inches, taken at a depth of over 2500 fathoms. This is a most unusual size for a fish from the great depths. Large fish are exceptional among the population of the abyssal depths, where the opportunities for a good feed must be rare indeed, as indicated by the great size of the mouths of most of the fish living there, which is in general quite out of proportion to their length. Our last haul on the expedition was made on September 15, 1948, to the southwest of the British Isles. Four genuine

Fig. 11.—*Umbellula* from the
Romanche Channel.

bottom fish, two specimens of *Echinomacrurus mollis* and two of *Bathypterois longipes,* the latter characterized by the great length of its fin rays, were caught at a depth of 2700 fathoms.

In summing up the main results, Nybelin states that, from the nine most successful hauls at depths exceeding 2200 fathoms, no fewer than 60 specimens of abyssal bottom fish, representing 14 different species, were obtained. Half a score of these had only once before been caught by other expeditions, including the *Grimaldich-tys profundissimus,* which was caught twice from the *Albatross,* both times at depths exceeding 3000 fathoms. Many of the fish and echinoderms were found both in the western and eastern Atlantic Valleys. This fact supports the view that the abyssal fauna are in general common to both valleys, *i.e.* that the mid-Atlantic Ridge which separates them is not a biological border-line. It appears extremely probable that even the very greatest ocean deeps are inhabited by living organisms, that is, that there is no zero-line of organic life at great depths. Definite proof of this conclusion by our expedition can be expected from the great Danish circumnavigating expedition now under way on the *Galathea.* The equipment of that fine ship includes the electric winch from the *Albatross* and its spare steel cables.

Chapter 22

THE VIRGIN ISLANDS, AND THE
DEPTHS BEYOND

Leaving astern the wild barren rocks of St. Paul's and
the crowd of indignant sea-birds hovering over the dere-
lict lighthouse, we again steered west along the Equator.
For the second time we approached the western Atlantic
Valley. A year earlier we had crossed it in a hurry, for
fear of the West Indian hurricanes. This time it was not
an atmospheric but an economic low which made us
speed on. Time was against us and our money was ebbing fast. Nevertheless, we decided we must examine this
alluring part of the ocean bed, almost unexplored by
earlier investigators.

A series of minor mishaps thwarted our first attempts.
After a few trawls the steel cable got so twisted that the
next shot with the long coring-tube failed because of
the spinning movement imparted to the instrument by
the residual twist. Still, a couple of very interesting cores
were raised from depths of nearly 2500 fathoms. To our
great surprise one of them contained, below some 15
feet of typical fine-grained deep-sea sediment, layers of
sand resembling the delta sand found in river estuaries.

Still more noteworthy was the fact that below one of the sand layers there was an accumulation of vegetable remains, tiny twigs and small nuts from monocotyledonous bushes or trees, indicating influx from some river estuary. The nearest one, that of the great Amazon, lies about 500 nautical miles to the southwest, in the direction to which the prevailing surface current runs, which makes this find still more puzzling. According to a rough estimate of the rate of sedimentation, the layer in question should have been deposited at least two hundred thousand years ago. Could a radical change in the ocean surface currents have taken place in such a relatively—geologically speaking—recent past? Or, still more improbable, could the distance from the South American continent have been so much less at that time that the outflow of one of its rivers reached this remote spot? These are problems for the investigators at present engaged in attempts to decipher this remarkable sample from the records of the deep.

The bottom profile persisted in presenting disturbing irregularities—hills and scarps with sudden changes in level. These certainly did not encourage either trawling or coring operations. Sediment soundings by depth-charges also failed over this rugged bottom because of a multitude of diffuse echoes thrown back against protuberances and precipices masking the fainter echoes from the bottom below the bottom. But Nybelin, in one of his successful hauls, obtained quite a number of queer sea-pens of the genus *Umbellula*, mentioned before, which bear a tuft of feather-like, strongly phosphorescent polyps at a height of several feet above the bottom. Their faint illumination thrown over the deep-sea floor must present an eerie sight to the rare stragglers through those regions, the deep-sea fish and their prey.

On August 11th, we reached the idyllic harbor of the island of St. Thomas—called Charlotte Amalie after a queen of Denmark. These small islands, the last remnant of the Danish colonies, were ceded for a consideration to the United States in 1917. With its Danish street names and with statues of Danish royalty adorning its market-places, this little town right in the tropics reminded us curiously of far-off Denmark. The impression was heightened when we were addressed in pidgin-Danish by some of the older dark-skinned natives.

During the golden century of cane sugar and unlimited consumption of rum this colony was a source of considerable revenue to the Danish crown. This affluence, made possible through slave labor, lasted only until 1849, when the Danes abolished slavery. This generous gesture ruined the sugar mills and the rum distilleries and, incidentally, led to great misery among the liberated slaves, who, as a rule, had been well treated by their owners. Since then, the islands have not been able to pay their own way and the United States has found their possession an unsuccessful business from an economic point of view. Moreover, the colored population has become infected by a democracy of a rather inferior brand and its political bosses are mostly out for plunder. "A heaven for climate and a hell for politics" is a descriptive phrase that fits the Virgin Islands. At the time of our visit the Governor was a Negro, an intelligent and cultured lawyer who had had a brilliant career in the United States. He had a tough job in keeping the vociferous and voracious leaders of the political parties in check, added to the difficulties of improving the economic condition of the islands.

One of the worst drawbacks is the shortage of fresh water, which has led to the building of costly reservoirs for collecting the run-off from the steep, eroded hills. One remedy proposed for the water shortage is to utilize solar heat in large distillation plants, in which sea-water pumped up from the shore would be converted into drinkable water. This most interesting scheme was put forward, according to what I was told, by an inventive lady engineer of the Massachusetts Institute of Technology. At present the price of water, which we on the *Albatross* had to buy in large quantities, is two dollars per metric ton. Still, to go over from distilling rum to distilling sea-water seemed something of a come-down to us thirsty northerners.

After having worked through the accumulated mail which lay awaiting me at St. Thomas, and written the inevitable answers, I paid a flying visit to the neighboring island of St. Croix. It appeared even more idyllic than St. Thomas and equally full of memories of the good old Danish times. The towns are named Christiansted and Frederiksted. Danish is commonly spoken and all the inhabitants delighted in hearing our northern tongue and treated us as old friends. A motor trip brought us up to the summit of a densely forested hill crowned by an old sugar mill, which an American millionaire has converted into a quaint and rather charming summer resort. The view from the top of this sugar castle was magnificent, and so were the flower gardens surrounding it. Most of the other hills were also crowned by old sugar mills, evidence of the industry and wealth of a past age.

Returning by plane to St. Thomas and to our good *Albatross,* we made ready for the last lap of our long voyage. Leaving the idyll of Charlotte Amalie behind us, we steered north for the great deep, an extension of the famous Puerto Rico Trench. There the American cruiser *Milwaukee,* just before World War II, had sounded the record depth of the whole Atlantic Ocean, 9210 meters or 5035 fathoms. We could not afford the time which would have been required to reach this position, nor did we have at our disposal the length of steel cable necessary for working our long core-samplers down to this depth, or for making a haul with the trawl. So we had to limit ourselves to the eastern branch of this deep trench in which, according to some geologists, the material for a yet unborn mountain chain is being accumulated.

Delayed by an adverse wind and surface current, we did not reach the spot chosen for our most hazardous enterprise, trawling at a depth of over 4000 fathoms, until the afternoon of August 18th. The depth along the course chosen for our haul varied between 4200 and nearly 4400 fathoms, so that an extension cable had to be spliced on to the end of our ordinary coring cable, making a total length of more than 6500 fathoms. The trawl reached the bottom at midnight and, after a haul of nearly four hours, was again raised to the surface, the whole operation taking nearly nineteen hours. The difficulties inherent in such work have been set forth already, as well as the catch from this record haul. Although meager, it fulfilled one of the main purposes of our biological work, namely, proving that even at this enormous depth bottom-living organisms exist, and that, therefore, the existence of a depth limit to marine life is highly doubtful. Time and other circumstances did not permit any further work at similar depths, and the *Albatross* was steered north-north-west in order to work in the red clay area of the northwestern Atlantic.

There, at a depth of 3200 fathoms to the southeast of Bermuda, we raised a core of special interest. It was

taken by means of a coring-tube of wide bore, in order
to obtain more material from each layer penetrated.
The length of this large corer had to be limited to only
20 feet. The uppermost layer of the core we raised was
a relatively hard crust, made up mostly of the oxides of
iron and manganese. The soft parts of the core beneath
it displayed an astonishing variety of colors, ranging
from dark slate-gray to green with patches of bright yellow, and much of it was chocolate brown. It contained
a number of stones, the largest weighing well over a
pound, a most unusual occurrence at such great depths.
Petrographic and mineralogical examination has later
proved the stones to be of gabbroid character, probably
derived from the bed-rock of the ocean and not of continental origin. A closer investigation now under way has
afforded an insight into the little-known chemistry of
the great deeps and the submarine weathering process
going on there.

Some distance farther west from this position, where
the Admiralty chart is marked "Mn," signifying that
the bottom is rich in manganese, we made a last attempt
to secure some of the interesting potatoes of the ocean
bed, namely, manganese concretions. An earlier attempt,
made with our large dredge in the central Pacific Ocean,
had failed and led to the loss of the equipment. Not
without misgivings I had our remaining large sledge-net
or dredge hauled along the bottom at a depth of over
3000 fathoms. It narrowly escaped the fate of its predecessor. Raised above deck, the big sack of netting was
found to be badly torn, probably by some rock passing
straight through it. But to my great joy, two smaller net-
bags attached to the dredge had remained intact and
contained more than two hundred of the precious manganese nodules I had been hoping for. Most of them

were quite small, but a number of larger concretions were also included in the catch and will afford most welcome material for studies and analyses in the laboratory. Greatly pleased with this stroke of luck at the eleventh hour, I gave orders for setting our course to the east, heading for European waters and home.

Chapter 23

THE MYSTERY OF DEEP-SEA RADIUM

One of the greatest mysteries opened up by science in the past sixty years is that of radium, of other radio-active elements and of their disintegrating atoms. The study of this momentous discovery in the middle 1890's has led to a revolution in a number of sciences—physics, chemistry, geology, general geophysics, cosmic physics, astronomy, etc. The enormous energy set free in radio-active disintegrations and, more recently, in the controlled fission of the heaviest atoms, those of uranium and plutonium, has not only explained how the stars generate their stupendous torrents of radiant energy but has also, unfortunately, led to the construction of the atom bomb and its inherent threat to civilization. Similarly, our notions about the age of our Earth and the origin of its geothermal heat have been profoundly modified. In addition, geologists have used the radio-active atoms of uranium and thorium as immutable time-keepers or hour-glasses, from which they can read the age of rocks containing these elements and the final products of their immensely slow breakdown, lead and helium gas. Thanks to these radioactive age-determinations, we now know that the oldest rocks so far investigated were solidified from a molten state about two billion years ago and that the Earth itself is consequently still older, possibly by as much as another billion years.

The wide dissemination of radioactive elements in the Earth's crust, revealed by the extraordinary sensitivity of electrical methods, indicated that these elements are in general much more concentrated within the planet's outermost crust, especially in its granite layer, than in the deeper strata. There are strong reasons for believing, although without direct evidence to support it, that the very core of our Earth, assumed to consist mainly of nickel-iron, is extremely poor in radioactive elements, just as are the iron meteorites falling onto the Earth's surface from interplanetary space.

Considering this general falling-off in radium content from the surface downward, it was the more puzzling that some of the deepest ocean deposits, like red clay, are fairly rich in radium, with contents exceeding those of granitic continental rocks in the proportion of ten, or even twenty, to one.

This anomaly of the great ocean depths being much richer in radium than the continental crust I had thought about a great deal. Nearly twenty years ago a systematic search for the source of abyssal radium was started in Sweden in co-operation with specialists from Norway and Austria. Special methods had to be worked out for measuring the tiny content of radium and of its ancestor, uranium, in sea-water. Uranium was found to be present in a fairly constant concentration of 1.3 parts in 1,000,000,000 parts of water. Its descendant radium—which in the rocks where it is produced from uranium stands in a fixed proportion of about one part in

3,000,000—is, comparatively speaking, much rarer in ocean waters, which generally contain only 10 to 20 per cent of this equilibrium amount. Hence there must be some mechanism for transferring the radium from the water to the bottom deposits.

The riddle was solved by considering the immediate mother element of radium, ionium, itself a great-great-granddaughter of uranium. This element, owing to its chemical properties, is liable to become precipitated together with iron which is present in an unstable state in sea-water; thus the greater the depth, *i.e.* the height of the superposed water column, out of which the precipitation takes place, the greater the concentration of ionium found.

This precipitation of ionium from sea-water to the bottom and the subsequent production of ionium-supported radium is of great interest *per se*. For as thousands of years pass and more and more sediment rich in ionium is added to the bottom layer, the strata in a long core must with increasing age—that is, with increasing depth below the sediment surface—show characteristic variations in their radium content. Thus a layer about 10,000 years old should hold a maximum of ionium-supported radium, whereas farther down a regular decline should set in as the ionium disintegrates, to 50 per cent in 80,000 years, to 25 per cent in 160,000 years, and so on. Theoretically, therefore, the radium content in the cores would be halved, compared with the surface value, in a layer 80,000 years old, and reduced to one-fourth in a layer twice as old. Thus radium measurements as an indicator of the ionium content—which it is much more difficult to measure—would serve as a highly desirable means of finding the age of the different strata and from these it should be possible to work out values for the rate of sedimentation. In certain cases this has actually been found possible. Thus in a core taken by the *Albatross* in the central Pacific Ocean north of Tahiti from a depth of 2700 fathoms, the sharp decrease in radium content from the surface downward made it possible to work out the rate of sedimentation during the past twenty to thirty thousand years. The value found was extremely low, namely, less than half a millimeter or about one-fiftieth part of an inch in 1000 years. (Fig. 12.)

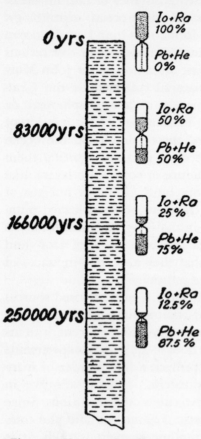

Fig. 12.—Change of radium content of cores with age.

Unfortunately, in many cases the regular distribution of radium in the cores is disturbed by secondary influences—diffusion acting through thousands of years. The great hopes originally set on radioactive measurements as a master key to the chronology of the deep-sea sediments do not seem likely to be fulfilled, except in rare cases where the disturbing influences mentioned have not been dominant.

Here is another interesting instance of radium measurements as indicators of deep-ocean chronology. Among the most curious formations found on the ocean floor are the so-called manganese nodules or concretions already referred to and first described by Sir John Murray and Renard from material collected by the *Challenger* Expedition. Generally of a semi-spherical or ellipsoidal shape, varying in diameter from a fraction of an inch to several inches, these growths on the ocean bed very much resemble dirty potatoes. Cutting them through, one finds a structure of concentric layers, like the rings on a tree stump, built around a nucleus of heterogeneous origin—a fragment of water-logged pumice or a shark's tooth, it may be. Chemical analysis proves that the nodules consist largely of iron and manganese oxides, but that they also contain traces of other elements, including radium.

From investigations of deposits near thermal sources on land, it is known that radium has a kind of affinity for manganese and follows the latter element into its concretions. This affinity goes so far that, as experiments made in Göteborg have proved, a fine powder of manganese superoxide, "braunstein," is most effective in removing radium from extremely weak solutions. Since radium enters the concretions alone, without the company of its supporting mother element ionium, it is bound to decay at the rate characteristic of isolated radium preparations—50 per cent in the course of seventeen centuries, to 25 per cent in 3400 years, and so on.

Removing thin layers from the surface of a large manganese nodule the superficial radium content of which was very high (in fact, several times higher than that of the surrounding sediment), I found that the radium values fell off rapidly with "depth" below the nodule surface. At a depth of between one and two millimeters, only half the surface content was found, and at about three millimeters in depth, only one-fourth. Assuming each fresh layer added to the concretion to have originally been as rich in radium as its present surface, one easily finds the rate of radial growth of the concretion to be about one millimeter in 1000 years. At this rate, in order to attain its present diameter of about two inches, the manganese nodule must have been growing for about 25,000 years. Thus the potato crop on the fields of the deep ocean ripens very slowly indeed.

Finally, one prevalent illusion disseminated by irresponsible journalists should be dispelled. Measurements of the amount of uranium in deep-sea deposits have yielded very low values, quite as low as those found in ordinary sedimentary rocks from the continents. There is consequently not the remotest chance of obtaining uranium from the great depths of the oceans, and the science of the ocean floor cannot be accused of catering to an increased production of atom bombs.

Another journalistic sensation, which hardly requires to be refuted after the underwater explosions at Bikini, is that the detonation of an atom bomb may set up a chain reaction transmuting the immense supply of hydrogen in the water into helium. Such a chain reaction, involving all oceanic hydrogen, would make a hydrogen bomb out of our small planet, converting it into a dazzling nova, a fate which will assuredly not overtake us, whatever new devilry our nuclear scientists may be capable of turning out.

On the other hand, the explosion of an atom bomb near the ocean floor at great depths would afford a splendid opportunity for studying the rocky substratum by seismic methods and would, moreover, be perfectly harmless. Let us hope that the present supply of atom bombs may one day be turned to such useful purposes, instead of scorching and irradiating to death the innocent inhabitants of the world's largest cities.

Chapter 24

WITH THE *ALBATROSS* TO LONDON
AND TO GÖTEBORG

A visit to London on our return voyage had been planned while the expedition was still in the Indian Ocean. Leading oceanographers in Britain, the Royal Society, and the Hydrographic Department of the Admiralty—all, prior to the cruise, had given me great help and encouragement. This, I felt, put us under an obligation to take the *Albatross* to the city from which the famous *Challenger* cruise had been launched. We had a special reason for wishing to do so. All attempts made to prolong the existence of the *Albatross* as a deep-sea research ship, with her equipment intact, had failed. After the return of the expedition, she was to be reconverted into a combined freighter and training-ship, and all her costly equipment was to be taken out of her and stored ashore. It was therefore the last opportunity for showing our tools of research and the results obtained with them to our British colleagues.

There were, however, financial difficulties connected with this detour and the delay it would entail in our return to Göteborg. These difficulties were overcome, thanks to the generosity of the owners. The energetic Director of the Swedish Institute in London for Anglo-Swedish cultural relations, Dr. Asta Kihlbom, had done all in her power to promote the plan, and had elicited an invitation to our expedition from the Port of London Authority by way of its Chairman, Sir John Anderson. The offer included the promise of a distinguished berth in the Shadwell Docks during our visit to London. Various learned societies had stated that their members were interested in visiting the ship and seeing her equipment. Our arrival had been scheduled for September 23rd, and we had the usual misgivings that adverse winds and currents, which are often encountered in approaching the English Channel, would unduly delay us.

In spite of these cares, a number of coring and trawling operations were carried out during our third and last crossing of the North Atlantic Ocean. On September 5th, Kullenberg and Jonasson were successful in getting a coring-tube over 60 feet long, while working at a depth of 2500 fathoms, with excellent results. A second attempt made at a distance of ten nautical miles from the first station failed because of a slight mishap with the release. Instead, a depth-charge of six pounds of T.N.T., the heaviest charge used during the whole cruise, was exploded at a depth of 1400 fathoms. Unfortunately, the rugged character of the bottom profile gave rise to a host of spurious superficial echoes, so that none of the very deep echoes we had hoped for were evident on the record.

On a following day, Nybelin made a successful trawl at 2500 fathoms which brought up our largest bottom fish, a Macrura, *Nematonurus armatus.*

On September 13th, the echo-graph recorded a depth

of over 3200 fathoms, and so we took our last series of large-volume water samples suitable for radium and uranium determinations. We narrowly escaped a minor catastrophe, as the man at the oceanographic winch, weary after the night's work, by mistake put full speed on the winch instead of stopping it as the large water-bottle broke through the surface. In the nick of time he managed to stop the motor, or the precious instrument would have been torn off its wire when it met the meter wheel, an accident which had occurred nine months earlier and cost us the loss of a similar water-bottle now resting on the bottom of the Mindanao Trench.

On September 15th, Nybelin made his last haul with the trawl and was rewarded with a catch of four beautiful and rare bottom fish plus a number of invertebrate organisms. After that we considered our active assignment at sea finished, and set our course for the Lizard and for the cool northern waters beyond it.

Thanks to the excellent preparatory work done by the Swedish Institute and to the generous hospitality of the Port of London Authority, our visit to London was a great success. The six days we spent there were busy indeed. More than two hundred distinguished representatives of the many sciences interested in deep-sea work came on board to view the ship, its laboratories, the big winch, Kullenberg's piston corer and the Weibull plant for measuring the thickness of sediment by means of exploding depth-charges. In addition, Nybelin and Eriksson demonstrated chosen specimens from the abyssal fauna we had caught. Jerlov showed his optical methods for studying the sparsely distributed particles suspended in different water layers, while Koczy unrolled our long echo-grams showing the bottom profile over which we had been working.

The general public, too, had been kept informed about our cruise through a series of articles published in *The Times,* and took a lively interest in the visit of the *Albatross.* As it was obviously impossible to admit large crowds on board, we were invited instead to give radio talks on the expedition, through the B.B.C. A television demonstration from Alexandra Place was arranged, where some of the rare organisms from the great depths were shown on television for the first time. In general we felt that the *Albatross* cruise had stimulated great interest in the problems of the ocean floor, and that the new tools of research developed in Sweden would be used by future expeditions.

An important event during our visit was a lunch given by our Captain on board the *Albatross* at which we had a number of distinguished guests, among them Admiral Sir John Edgell and Admiral Sir Guy Wyatt, the past and present hydrographers to the Admiralty; the Deputy Master of Trinity House; the Director of the Discovery Department at the Colonial Office; and the Director of the Swedish Institute. The occasion was celebrated by opening the precious bottle of old Madeira which had been carried twice around the world, first by the *Challenger* and then by the *Albatross,* and which had been given to me by Mr. Grabham of Funchal. The donor's health was drunk in the old wine he had so generously bestowed on our expedition.

On the evening of September 29th, the *Albatross* left the Port of London and our many friends there and set out on her homeward course across the North Sea, arriving safely in the harbor of Göteborg on October 3rd, one day before the expiration of the fifteen months' lease allotted for the cruise. We men of science have in general not a very good reputation for punctuality, and a great part of the credit for our timely arrival must be accorded to the Captain and the officers of the ship who had managed it so well.

To say that our reception in our home port was warm-hearted is an understatement. We were honored with music from the Naval Base, ships in the harbor were covered with flags, sirens sounded and handkerchiefs waved from everywhere ashore. The quay where we landed held a throng of our relatives, friends and prominent citizens of Göteborg headed by our Chairman, Governor Jacobsson.

We had indeed been lucky. All members of the staff, the officers and the crew returned safe and sound. No serious illness had occurred on board and no life had been lost. Moreover, our program had, in the main, been successfully carried through. Some two hundred precious cores from the ocean floor containing unique records of the deep, with a total length of about one statute mile, were carefully preserved in the cool storage room of the ship. They will provide material for many years of painstaking laboratory work and measurements. Our immediate duty was to carry them and the rest of our harvest to the Oceanographic Institute, and to hand over the biological collections to the Natural History Museum of Göteborg, where Nybelin took charge of them.

The active work of the expedition was over. The much more lengthy, costly and laborious work of applying the most efficient methods of modern science to the study of our collections was to commence.

Chapter 25

THE HARVEST FROM THE OCEAN
DEPTHS

The *Albatross* Expedition was entirely a Swedish undertaking, planned in Sweden, carried out in a Swedish ship, using mainly a novel technique worked out in Sweden and financed by Swedish donors. The material collected from the depths of three oceans, on the other hand, is so vast that only by means of international co-operation can it be completely worked up and analyzed. In a dozen scientific institutions both in Europe and in the United States, samples from our long cores, carefully chosen and prepared, are being analyzed by eminent specialists in the different sciences involved. This wholehearted co-operation from our colleagues, both in Sweden and abroad, is one of our greatest assets and a stimulus for future work.

The Oceanographic Institute of Göteborg, where the expedition was planned and where most of the methods and instruments had been evolved, serves as a center of organization from which the samples are distributed and where the results from the analyses are received and tabulated. It is essential that the precious cores, the abstracts from the records of the deep, which have been taken at such high cost in time, labor and money, should be carefully preserved against desiccation and mixing of layers from different levels. Unless properly cared for until they can be analyzed by specialists, they may well prove an "embarrassment to their owner," as an English authority recently put it. On the other hand, if well preserved and judiciously sampled, they afford a wealth of information on the sediments covering the least accessible and least known part of the Earth's crust, the deep ocean floor, revealing its past history and the geochemical and geophysical transformations which have occurred within the carpet of sediment deposited during millions of years.

Apart from the laborious and time-consuming descriptive, preparative and sampling work on the cores, the investigations in Göteborg have been mainly concentrated on the microchemical composition of the cores, on their content of radium and of its ancestor element uranium, the latter investigation having also been carried out in the Radium Institute of Vienna. Further, certain microfossils such as foraminifera and, especially, radiolarians, are being studied in Göteborg. Specialists from Australia, Austria and France are engaged in this work, along with members of the Swedish staff. Institutes in Stockholm and in Uppsala have undertaken geological, mineralogical and spectrographical analyses. In the laboratories at Kagghamra near Stockholm, Dr. G. Arrhenius, geologist to the expedition, has done splendid work on the cores from the eastern Pacific Ocean and has opened new perspectives on the intricate problems of their stratigraphy. Arrhenius' work, which is now being printed as a separate volume of the Expedition Reports, has evoked most favorable comment from foreign authorities visiting Sweden. His father, Dr. O. Arrhenius, has undertaken the arduous task of analyzing some 16,000 representative samples from all our cores for certain chemical elements of special interest.

On the European continent, Professor Correns of Göttingen, an acknowledged master of deep-sea sediment research, is having two of our most interesting cores from the equatorial part of the North Atlantic Ocean analyzed. Another leading authority on submarine geology, Professor Kuenen of Groningen in Holland, has undertaken to supervise the work on our Indonesian cores, the mineralogical study of which has been confided to Dr. Doeglas of Wageningen. In Ghent, Belgium, Professor W. Dekeyser is working on the X-ray analysis of samples from two long, deep cores of red clay, one from the northwest Atlantic, the other from the central Pacific Ocean. At the Sorbonne, Professor Cailleux and Mlle. Duplaix are examining the deep-sea sand from Mediterranean cores. In Vienna, analyses of the uranium and radium content in sea-water samples and in deep-sea deposits are being carried out under the direction of the chief of the Radium Institute, Professor Berta Karlik. At the Natural History Museum of Milan, Professor Fausto Lona has kindly undertaken to examine samples from our Tyrrhenian cores for pollen grains from the surrounding shores, which in certain layers are present in great numbers and in an excellent state of preservation.

Besides the work in Stockholm and Göteborg, examination of the foraminiferan shells as indicators of past climatic changes has been carried out by Dr. W. Schott of Hanover, by Dr. F. Phleger of the Scripps Oceanographic Institute in La Jolla, California, and by Mr. C. Ovey of the British Museum (Natural History), London.

On this last-named investigation, which is being carried out in collaboration with Dr. J. Wiseman of the same Museum, a few remarks appear appropriate.

Working on a core from the equatorial Atlantic, taken from a region where sedimentation appears to have suffered a minimum of disturbances from extraneous factors, Wiseman and Ovey claim to have found a surprisingly simple relation between the percentage of lime present at different levels and the surface temperature prevailing at the time when the layer was deposited. From these studies it appears that about 117,000 B.C. a rapid fall in temperature set in, which was followed nearly forty thousand years later by a maximum temperature. After that, a new period of cold began, although not quite so severe as the preceding one, and reached its maximum about 68,000 B.C. Then temperature again rose to a climatic optimum, at around 43,000 B.C., and remained warm for some sixteen thousand years. After that followed a third decline to a minimum, about 23,000 B.C., not quite so severe as the two preceding ones. Afterward the temperature rose, fell and rose again, reaching a new climatic optimum which prevailed between the years 7000 and 3000 B.C., after which world temperature, as indicated by the records of the deep, receded to its present medium level.

The main features of these climatic changes are in agreement with what geologists have outlined in their study of recent glacial and interglacial periods on the continents, but the dating is much more precise. If Wiseman's and Ovey's results are confirmed by further studies of the foraminifera in equally favorably situated cores, a new era will be opened both in palaeoclimatology and in the chronology of the ocean floor. The span of time over which such studies can be extended is naturally limited by the length of the cores so far obtained and by the rate of deposition of the calcareous sediments, which is fairly high. It is, however, not impossible that clues similar to those afforded by the pelagic foraminifera may be obtained also from the study of other microfossils present in the red clay, especially radiolarians and diatoms. If such be the case, submarine records might serve for extending the palaeoclimatic work back into the Tertiary Age, during which the lower parts of our red-clay cores, especially those from the Pacific Ocean, were deposited.

One problem of special interest is the bottom temperature of the oceans during the Tertiary Age. From evidence obtained on land, the climate then should have been considerably warmer than during the succeeding Quaternary Age with its several glacial periods, so that ice-caps in the polar regions should have been either absent or of much less extent than at present. In such an event the present ice-cold temperature of the bottom water, mainly derived from the Antarctic, would not have occurred during the Tertiary Age, and a higher temperature, similar to that at present found in the Mediterranean depths, would have prevailed over the ocean floor. Such a warm period, extending over millions of years, must have left its mark also on bottom organisms which at that time were living at a temperature perhaps ten degrees higher than at present. It remains for future research, of the kind Arrhenius has started with his investigations of the long cores from the eastern Pacific, to confirm or to refute this hypothesis of a warm Tertiary period in the oceanic depths.

The study of the cosmic components present in the deepest deposits, namely the cosmic spherules, and perhaps also the nickel contained in the sediment in a dispersed state, may produce information regarding the past cosmic history of our planet, notably on variations in the bombardment by bullets from the cosmos, meteors and meteoritic dust. It does not appear improbable that extensive research on the intensity of the Earth's magnetic field in great ocean depths, such as are on the schedule of the Danish *Galathea* Expedition, may lead to the discovery of local magnetic anomalies near the ocean floor, where may be buried giant meteors such as those which have pockmarked the moon and left big craters on the continents.

Weibull's studies of the thickness of the sediment carpet by means of reflected echoes from exploding depth-charges have recently been perfected to such a degree that reflecting surfaces in the sediment only ten meters apart now can be recorded. Combining such investigations with those made by the refraction method, where sound waves following a generally horizontal path in the sediment or in the substratum are recorded, will increase our knowledge of the structure of both considerably. Already it seems fairly certain, through work carried out by Ewing and others, that the bed-rock beneath the sediment carpet is mainly basaltic in nature and thus different from the granitic rocks predominating on land. The hidden topography of this oceanic bed-rock may be revealed by using Weibull's depth-charges, preferably dropped from a helicopter hovering near the surface of the sea.

Important results are being obtained through Jerlov's analysis of his optical measurements made from the *Albatross*. The extremely small suspended particles, revealed by an intense Tyndall cone of light in samples taken from different depths, give information on the water movement, both near the surface and at great depths. Also Koczy's studies of the water layers immediately above the bottom have thrown a new light on the little-known interaction between the sediment and the water in contact with it. Radium and uranium analyses of sea-water and of the sediment layers in cores from great depths afford a hopeful although rather complicated approach to their chronological problem and to the rate of sedimentation.

Mineralogical studies of the rare stones sometimes brought up from great depths by means of a wide-bore coring-tube are being carried out by Mellis in Stockholm. They have given a conclusive answer to the much debated question whether rocks and stones in great depths are liable to undergo a submarine weathering. Studies by the same scientist of the layers of volcanic ash in cores from the Mediterranean have already been mentioned as being of special interest to archaeologists.

Adding to these analyses of sea-water and of deep-sea deposits the results of the biological work in the North Atlantic, now being published, one is justified in saying that the *Albatross* brought back a rich harvest of new and important observations from the three oceans. When the study of this material has been completed and the results published, our knowledge of the ocean floor will be considerably increased.

The new technique of deep-sea research developed in Sweden and elsewhere has thrown open a vast field of work in which specialists from half a score of different sciences can co-operate in solving hitherto unapproachable problems, in physical and chemical oceanography, in the geophysics of the Earth's crust, in submarine geology, in petrography and mineralogy, in geochemistry, palaeontology, palaeoclimatology and deep-sea biology, and in the sciences of archaeology and of astronomy. Undoubtedly the deep ocean floor is now coming into the forefront as a field for future research. Two new deep-sea expeditions, the Danish with the *Galathea* and the British with the *Discovery II,* are now under way. Both these expeditions are using the techniques developed for the *Albatross* cruise.

The field of work is so enormous that it calls for international co-operation in planning and for exchange of technical improvements and of results obtained. A step in this direction taken by the Scandinavian countries is the setting up of a joint committee for planning and carrying out deep-sea work with a special research ship equipped for the purpose. Such co-operation would make it possible to carry out investigations and analyze the material obtained without too large a financial strain on each of the participating countries.

At the beginning of this century, an international organization was created on Swedish initiative for the study of the waters around northwest Europe and of its important fishing grounds—the International Council for the Investigation of the Sea, with headquarters in Copenhagen. It has survived two world wars and is still active. The time now seems ripe for creating similar co-operation in the study of the much vaster field of the deep ocean. Much greater efforts will be required than in shallow-water research. On the other hand, even more important results of pure scientific interest may be expected. In such co-operation Great Britain and the United States, the two greatest seafaring nations of the world, seem predestined to take leading parts.